CLICKING FOR MR. RIGHT

Seeking Love in the
Second Half of Life
in the E-trenches of
Online Dating

JENNA DEBORAH CASSELL

Capucia LLC
211 Pauline Drive #513
York, PA 17402
www.capuciapublishing.com
Send questions to: support@capuciapublishing.com

Paperback ISBN: 978-1-954920-17-0
eBook ISBN: 978-1-954920-47-7
Library of Congress Control Number: 2022921131

Cover Design: *Ranilo Cabo*
Layout: *Ranilo Cabo*
Editor and Proofreader: *Jennifer Crosswhite*
Book Midwife: *Carrie Jareed*

Printed in the United States of America

Capucia LLC is proud to be a part of the Tree Neutral® program. Tree Neutral offsets the number of trees consumed in the production and printing of this book by taking proactive steps such as planting trees in direct proportion to the number of trees used to print books. To learn more about Tree Neutral, please visit treeneutral.com.

CONTENTS

Prologue   1

Introduction   5

Chapter 1   Maybe I'm Being Too Picky?   7
Chapter 2   The End   9
Chapter 3   The Invitation   13
Chapter 4   Weekly Breakfast   17
Chapter 5   The Yellow Bug   23
Chapter 6   Overhaul   29
Chapter 7   The Escape Vehicle   37
Chapter 8   Sunday Times   43
Chapter 9   In a Family Way   47
Chapter 10   Three's a Crowd   57
Chapter 11   Looking for Red Flags   63
Chapter 12   The Wedding Escort   69
Chapter 13   A Singles' Affair   75
Chapter 14   Bob's Big Boy   85
Chapter 15   Expectations or Anxiety?   89
Chapter 16   Speedy Seniors   95
Chapter 17   Moonless Night   107
Chapter 18   Where the Boys Are   115
Chapter 19   Watercooler Waltzing   119
Chapter 20   Search Optimization   129

Chapter 21	A Picture's Worth a Thousand Dreams	133
Chapter 22	Who Needs a Man?	139
Chapter 23	Virtual Virtuoso	143
Chapter 24	Great Expectations…Revisited	149
Chapter 25	Invitation to Dinner…or Booty Call?	157
Chapter 26	Doctor, Lawyer, Indian Chief	161
Chapter 27	Praying for Patience	167
Chapter 28	Who Wears the Pants?	175
Chapter 29	Breaking up Is Hard to Do… Unless You Have a Smart Phone	181
Chapter 30	Two-Thousand-Mile Date	185
Chapter 31	Can I Get a Ride?	195
Chapter 32	What's It All About, Jocelyn?	199
Epilogue		203

PROLOGUE

Not long after arriving in San Diego in the late 1990s, I met a phenomenal woman at the baby shower of someone neither of us knew very well. While not moms ourselves, Jenna Cassell and I both loved kids, people, and life. We became instant "sista-friends" and happily bonded as edgy, entrepreneurial women.

Jenna was an early pioneer in the use of video and online media technologies to teach American Sign Language. In 1987 she founded Sign Enhancers Inc., which continues today as the gold standard in ASL education and resources. Simultaneously, she grew to be a worldwide legend for the stunning artistry and mastery of her work as an interpreter. I never forgot meeting Amanda, a young woman who had learned ASL through Jenna's materials. She could hardly believe I had the great master's number in my phone and was blown away to call and later work with her!

As sistas, and Jewish to boot, Jenna and I talked a lot about our love lives. Neither of us quite got with the settle-down-and-have-kids program, as I'm gay, so marriage wasn't even an option until 2013, and she was extremely hurt when her deaf partner of twenty-five years unexpectedly left. I cannot even count the tears, laughs, and worries we shared riding the wildly promising and disappointing waves of relationships.

Recovering from her divorce, Jenna got together with Loui Pane, a kind-hearted guy with a goofy sense of humor who absolutely adored her. They were on-and-off, in-and-out-and-always-back-again companions for over two decades. All the while, Jenna was candid about carrying out an online search and clicking away for the man she dreamed might be more Mr. Right. The vignettes in this volume are rendered hilariously and profoundly, as she describes her often quirky quest for the perfect person so many of us fervently seek yet rarely find. Is such a mate a figment of imagination, or perhaps right in front of us if we could only let them be?

Jenna and I both spent time in Southern California and south Florida, so I had frequent front-row access to her dating tales and short-lived romances. Several times she had me so convinced of her latest miraculous match that I itched with jealousy. Once she even called to tell, and ask, me about a possible female flame. But things always had a way of fizzling fast, while news and visits from Loui were caring and constant.

In the year before COVID set in, Jenna moved back to San Diego and into Loui's loving arms. It was such a bright, sweet, happy time as they enjoyed traveling abroad and made the trip to city hall to get married! But then, out of the blue, they were struck with the terrifying news that Jenna had a brain tumor, the deadly glioblastoma type. She had brain surgery the week of the initial pandemic shutdown, followed by intensive chemo and radiation treatments.

I knew how much Jenna loved this book she was almost done writing. And that her brain power and language centers were in an uncertain, harrowing decline. Traversing the very rocky and scary terrain of brain cancer, she still had two chapters to finish. None of us can anticipate such an ordeal, and I wanted somehow to help.

Enlisting Amanda's bilingual English and ASL skills, it was fascinating to discover that the signing centers in Jenna's brain worked better than her verbal vocabulary. Through combined efforts, and Jenna's sheer passion and grit, she was able to complete the manuscript.

In Loui's endlessly loving care, Jenna passed away peacefully at home in December 2021. Her book mission was accomplished in the nick of time, with the editing and publishing assistance of Christine Kloser's Get Your Book Done company. When I called to say that Jenna was in her dying days, the manuscript was instantly emailed over. Within three days, a hard-copy proof was printed and express mailed so Jenna could hold her book in her hands! Thanks to the staff's willingness to work as needed with the unfolding what-ifs that last year, and Jenna's remarkable wits, these stories are now available for people to learn from and savor.

No words can possibly convey the feelings sitting by Jenna's bedside, reading this book aloud to her from my iPad, that first physical copy propped in her hospice bed. We will forever cherish the appreciative nods of her head, the tiny deep glints in her eyes, and all the brilliance and laughter that were her signature gifts.

While aching at losing Jenna far too soon, witnessing Loui's love throughout the years and through it all stands as the most heartfelt devotion and nurturing partnership a person could dream up or desire.

Click! Sure looks like Mr. Right!

Jamie Leno Zimron
Truckee, California, May 2022
Aikido Sensei, LPGA Pro, Psychologist, Speaker
www.TheCenteredWay.com

INTRODUCTION

Who would have imagined I had to revisit the rituals of my teenage years—at the ripe age of forty-five? To begin with, I never dreamed I would join the ranks of the mid-life brokenhearted, didn't see it coming, divorced-woman club. Truthfully, I didn't even know such a club existed, nor was I familiar with the rituals in which its members partook— among the most challenging… dare I say it… DATING.

Now, like handling most things in my life, I've kept an open mind and a positive attitude. I even signed up for online dating and joined an exclusive dating service that promised to "screen" the men carefully. It turns out they actually did eliminate men whose checks, made out to the dating service, had bounced.

Even for an avid online shopping guru like myself, "shopping" for a life partner on the internet was nothing short of bizarre. At first, I thought it was a gas, then it started giving me gas. It was a new hobby turned obsession, searching for "the one." I sat staring into the glow of the monitor, just clicking, clicking, clicking through the dozens, hundreds, even thousands of profiles. After a few weeks of this, I started looking for an organization called ODA, Online Dating Anonymous.

Online dating was insidious. This one had brown eyes. *Click.* That one didn't dance. *Click.* This one was too short. *Click.* That one didn't like dogs (a total deal breaker). *Click!* Even as exhaustion and disappointment set in, I remained convinced that Mr. Right was just one more mere mouse click away. *Click… Click… Click.* I'm sure that besides my relationship status woes, I also needed treatment for repetitive motion injury…in my clicking finger.

I mean, how hard could it be to find a man who is intelligent, forty-nine to fifty-nine years old, between five-foot-seven and six feet, honest, moral, nice, ready to commit, financially independent, well educated, married less than four times, has less than six children living at home, has a sense of humor and ability to communicate, lives within twenty-five miles of my city, for whom I would feel immediate chemistry, and who is not currently married or gay? Well, I only need ONE!

So, with my divorced sister as my expert dating coach, I bravely began with the emails, phone calls, and then—the most fear inducing of them all—the FIRST DATE.

What follows are the details of what transpired as I continued to click for Mr. Right. There were ups and downs, memorable dates for all the wrong reasons. But I kept at it and learned some surprising lessons along the way. The eternal optimist in me says this is a life lesson that will either lead all of us to connecting at long last to our true soul mates…or will teach us to love ourselves better in the process. Personally, I'm hoping it will do both.

Chapter 1

MAYBE I'M BEING TOO PICKY?

Journal entry:

So, what if I'm only 5'2" and he's 6'4"? If I reject him just for his extreme height, does this make me short -sighted as well as short of stature? Why should we care if people call us Mutt and Jeff or if I get a neck ache each time we dance? Or I'm doomed to forever lovingly gaze into his navel?

Maybe I shouldn't have counted that other one out so quickly just because he's wider than he is tall. Of course, I should have known something was up when all of his pictures were headshots... from the nose up.

Sometimes I wished I hadn't asked about that cute puppy in PuppyLuv4U's profile pictures. The answer was that Benji had been dead for twenty years. That meant Puppyluv was at least twenty years older than that picture. So yeah, the dog's gone, as was his hair and his teeth, his ability to drive at night. Even so, he probably does have a really good personality.

Is it too picky to eliminate the guys on MillionaireMatches. com who immediately confess, "One thing you should know: I'm not really a millionaire"?

I mean, is it too much to ask to meet a guy who doesn't need anger management, therapy, or have a murder charge in his past (even if he was acquitted of all charges by a jury of his peers)?

It's great that this one actually drives (bonus: at night!), but is it too much to hope to find a man who can see over the steering wheel and isn't quite so fluent in road rage? I mean, I can overlook some major resistible qualities including: bad comb-over, man boobs, huge stomach, bad teeth, lizard tongue, loud talking, and bad breath. But that last guy had them all!

I'll admit I'm not perfect, either. But I do upload profile pictures that show the real me, as I appear now. No Photoshop to remove flaws or stretching the image to give myself a few more inches in height and less in girth. I don't lie about my age or borrow my younger sister's photo. I don't put in cute dogs, dead fish, or fancy cars to take the attention off my physical attributes.

There's nothing in the description that requires a confession of any kind. Well, except for the unbelievably embarrassing fact that after years of looking for Mr. Right... I'm still here.

#Click#

Chapter 2

THE END

Jocelyn had a humiliating secret. She was one of *those* women. The ones who didn't see it coming.

"I love you," she told him daily.

For thirty-five years, Alex never failed to answer, "I love you more."

Jocelyn created an adventure of their soon-to-be retired life together. She envisioned the freedom of travel, the excitement of new places, and the romance of sharing it together.

Jocelyn lead him to their new American Indian couch to discuss her plans. She kissed him in a way that conveyed all the love and hopefulness she was feeling.

"We can do whatever we want," she said with arms open wide. "We've worked relentlessly for so long. Now finally, we're free to enjoy whatever we choose. Alex, what is it *you* want? We'll do whatever it is, go wherever you wish. What would make you most happy?"

His expression changed. His gaze dropped downward. Eyes filling with tears, his body slumped and convulsed into sobs. His shoulders quaked violently.

She was shocked. In all their years together, Jocelyn had only seen Alex cry once. In the hospital, where his mother lay on her death bed.

"What is it, honey?" Jocelyn reached to comfort him. "What's wrong?"

He tried to look at her, but his gaze went through her. "I'm, I'm unhappy, and I think I have to leave."

"What?" Surely, she'd misunderstood him. She prayed, if there were a merciful God, all time would rewind six seconds and now what would come out of his mouth would be, "Honey, what do you want for breakfast?"

But God did not intervene on her behalf in that moment. She held onto the sofa cushion to steady herself while he repeated his pronouncement. She felt every point of his words stabbing deep into her core, leaving her reeling and gasping for air. She'd suddenly been sucked into the vortex of her spouse's secret midlife crisis.

She got off the new couch and ran into the kitchen. She struggled for breath and gagged. Her stomach seized, and she vomited in her new farmhouse kitchen sink. Holding herself up, her fingers clenched the recently installed sea pearl granite countertop that was supposed to make their lives wonderful.

He sat motionless, staring ahead. Now, it was she who was shaking and sobbing uncontrollably. Yet, he didn't make a move to comfort her. It hit her hard; the man she had loved for a lifetime was already gone.

Just four short weeks later when he left for the last time, she did what she always did when he left their home. She hugged and kissed him. But as she was about to remind him to take his key with him, he handed it to her and walked away. She waited for him to turn and look back at her. He didn't.

The airport limo drove down the street. She stood waiting for the brake lights to go on. They didn't. She waited for him to return after a short ride around the block as he returned to his senses...and her. He didn't.

Jocelyn found herself alone in too big a world, living in too large a house, awakening each tortuous morning to the expanse of unused bed. She lay, as she had for more than three decades, on her side of their bed.

She had always wondered about *those* women, the ones who were shocked at being left. Before it happened to her, she never believed it was possible. How could you live with someone for thirty-five years and not know what he was thinking or feeling? How was it possible you didn't see the signs that he was unhappy, lying, or simply no longer present in the relationship? Of course, looking back, there were signs.

For all those years, Jocelyn had loved him beyond question. That's it. She didn't have a question. Perhaps if she had, the signs would have been the answer. In retrospect, they were everywhere. She simply never looked.

Jocelyn wanted to recover from this. To survive the hurt and loss. To reclaim what he'd taken from her when he got into that airport limo. Herself. Her life. Her identity.

They hadn't had children. He didn't want them. Now Jocelyn felt all those years of sacrifice with the coming of retirement. The emptiness of all his decisions for her life.

Jocelyn tried a string of ineffective therapists, read stacks of self-help books, leaned on friends with the hope of discovering that evasive secret of how to survive and move on.

Where to begin rebuilding her life? She barely let herself know that what she longed for was to go back in time to when she felt safe, happy, and loved. But there was no going back.

But at fifty-eight, technology had changed everything. Horrified by the thought, she found out the internet also played an integral part in seeking and finding romance. She'd never been scared of technology, but this had her staring at her keyboard with her hands frozen in her lap.

If Googling could get her life back, that's what she was going to do. The longing for a happy ending helped her make heroic strides in clicking her way into the modern dating world. As soon as her fingers could move to the keyboard.

#Click#

Chapter 3

THE INVITATION

This hit-and-run divorce rocked Jocelyn's world off its axis. Full of fear, she went to a therapist for support and a plan. Deborah was the same age as Jocelyn, with thirty years' experience as a marriage and family therapist. When Jocelyn saw Deborah's picture on her website, she felt like she was looking in the mirror. Both had long blonde hair, blue eyes, and clothing that was more comfortable than fashionable.

In their first meeting, Deborah got some basic information and Jocelyn's description of how Alex left.

After thinking for a few moments, Deborah said, "Many people expect it to be traumatic when a spouse dies. It's totally normal for the surviving spouse to be devastated and possibly grieving for years. Yet, it's not generally recognized that a divorce, such as yours, is very much like a sudden death. In some ways, it's worse. Because he didn't die. He unilaterally decided to just walk away. Jocelyn, how are you dealing with your husband's unexpected departure?"

Jocelyn's tears surprised her. She rarely cried in front of others. She tried to talk through the onslaught of emotions. "You're right. It feels like a death. He was my best friend, my partner in everything. The glue in my life. And now, he's just gone. I'm normally a strong and happy person. But now, the minute I wake up and remember he's gone, I'm filled with terror. He was my family for thirty-five years. Our relationship was the rock upon which I built my life. That rock is gone, and I feel afloat in the water with no land in sight."

"I understand. I'd like to help you see that this could be an opportunity to find out more about what you want to create for yourself in this new phase of life."

"New phase of life? It's the end of life as I know it."

"Yes. It's painful to recognize the door has closed on a very significant portion of how you've experienced your life. It will take time to heal from the shock and pain of it. We can work on finding ways to mourn and grieve in ways that help you go through the trauma of how this happened. At the same time, rather than always looking back, we can also work on ways to look ahead and move toward things that can begin to redefine and add new meaning to your life."

"I don't even know what those things would be. I just want to go back to normal. Find a new love and go back to living my life as it should be."

"That is a common reaction. It's one of the five stages of grief."

"Denial?"

"Yes. Exactly. While there is a great temptation to somehow 'go back,' the reality is this is actually an *invitation* to go forward. On to a new, perhaps even better life. Possibly with a new partner. But, Jocelyn, I'm going to suggest you first spend some time to learn about yourself. Develop a wholeness that may not have been available when you married so young. To walk through the fears you are experiencing and gain personal confidence. Only you can decide how to RSVP to this invitation."

"How do I get past this immobilizing fear?"

"There is only one way to get past it. That's through it. If you choose, I'll be here to help you navigate this new territory. Of course, the direction you take is up to you."

"What's the first step?"

"In your case, I'd recommend you do the very thing that terrifies you. Be alone. Let the goal be to learn about yourself. Spend one year doing only those things you want. Take your freedom and your wholeness back. Feel your own strength. Of course, you will have a support system for doing this. Your friends, family, and community. You'll meet new people as you do the things you love. Then, when the time is right, if you still want it, you can enter into a relationship. This time, it will be from a point of personal power and strength of knowing what you want. How do you feel about this?"

"Scared. But I know several of my friends who got married right after their divorces. They settled so they wouldn't be alone. Not too long afterwards, those marriages also ended. I know what you're saying is right. I will try to do this, with your help."

It was difficult as she was full of fear and anxiety, but Jocelyn committed to what her therapist had suggested. She wanted to feel at home alone in her house and in her own skin. She was unsure how she could survive a whole year trying to "get through" her new and intense anxiety. Since she'd married when she was twenty-three, she'd never experienced the freedom to do what she wanted, when she wanted. For the first time, her friends were of her own choosing. She was determined to surround herself with people who were positive, happy, and loving. Discover the things she loved to do. Create a new life. She accepted the invitation.

In the next twelve months, Jocelyn started dancing (something her husband would never do), yoga, writing, and enjoyed photography. She occasionally went to meetups where she met other women who also shared these interests. She joined a spiritual community and was surrounded by more friends than she ever had when she was married.

She continued to see Deborah once a month. She had developed her own support system and kept busy with work and her new interests. She felt a peacefulness that hadn't existed before. She even felt good spending a lot of alone time at home.

Now she was ready to begin dating again.

#Click#

Chapter 4

WEEKLY BREAKFAST

Dahlia and Jocelyn had just sat down for their weekly breakfast visit. Dahlia was her long-time bestie and closest ally in her post-divorce world. She had sun-colored yellow, shoulder-length hair and was always bright eyed with a wit that could help anyone survive anything. She had endured finding out about her own husband's infidelities and had to care for her children while simultaneously learning to care for herself. The two women shared everything and seemed to always be going through similar things at the same time. Even at the darkest times, they made each other laugh. They were like lifeboats for each other in a vast sea of turbulent waves.

Settled into their seats, they both started talking at once. Both stopped in mid-sentence and laughed.

"Will you remember yours if I go first?" Jocelyn asked.

"Yes. It's about a date that I've tried to erase from my memory, but it's burned in there. Please, after you." Dahlia motioned to Jocelyn.

"Thanks. I had an epiphany that will probably change our lives. But no guarantee I'll remember it in three minutes. Remember that old adage, 'If a tree falls in the forest and no one is there to hear it, does it still make a sound?'"

"Oh, yes," said Dahlia, "But I prefer to think of it as, 'If a man's lips are moving and you can't hear him, is he still lying?'"

Jocelyn laughed. "Yes. That will do too. I was thinking about how I've always believed if no one was there to witness my life, like a husband, I couldn't be happy. As if being alone would automatically translate as a failure."

Dahlia chimed in. "Well so many love songs, movies, and books in our culture perpetuate the idea. And my mother would totally agree with it too."

"But the truth is, the tree does make a sound. It doesn't need a witness. The flower that blooms in a vacant field opens its petals to reach for the sun's warmth, whether or not someone is there to see it. The river runs with wild abandon. It doesn't stop and wait for an audience. The trees dance with the wind, which blows just because that is exactly what it is meant to do.

"Lately, I've been catching myself enjoying my life. Alone. Solo. Literally dancing as if no one was watching. Laughing while reading a really good book. Enjoying a home-cooked meal I made just for myself. Going to the beach with an umbrella and boogie board in hand. Attending a ballet and sitting in the front row because there was just one seat available. Going to the movie of my choice and eating whatever I want. Watching the sun set behind the sparkling ocean and lingering there as long as I wish as brilliant colors morph the sky into an artist's canvas.

"For years, I've been listening to popular music, in which most songs are about pining for an old love, craving a new love, or just plain sad about not having a partner. I've been watching romantic comedies in which the formula requires a happy ending, always defined by the guy getting the girl and vice versa."

"Well, what's happy about each of them ending up alone?" Dahlia frowned.

"Exactly. That's my point. Most of us couldn't fathom the possibility that the leading woman might actually be better off not ending up with the leading man. Didn't you ever notice the movies always end as they pronounce their love and promise each other the 'happy ever after'? They never show you how, just maybe, when they're finally living together, he keeps her up all night with his snoring. Or when she returns from a fun shopping excursion with her girlfriend, he asks her, 'How much did you pay for *that*?' They don't show you how she begins to nag him about leaving his dirty socks all over the house."

"Oh, well, if I'm going to have to pick up someone's dirty socks, it's going to be my child's, not my husband's."

"Yes. Well, there are worse things. It's a known fact that fifty percent of first marriages fail. Sixty-seven percent of all second marriages and seventy-four percent of third marriages end in divorce. What's happening in the years leading up to those divorces?"

"A lot of unhappiness for both partners?"

"Yes. Infidelity, money problems, arguing, miscommunication, intimacy issues, among other things. I'm just saying compared to that, being single starts to look like a viable alternative.

"Would I rather find love with a gentle, loving partner? Settling for the wrong person can be a nightmare. Okay, you go now." Jocelyn pointed to Dahlia.

Dahlia said, "I know you're not finished. What else you got in there?" She pointed to her temple.

"Okay, I went to a concert," said Jocelyn.

"See? There are great things to do as a single," replied Dahlia.

"Wait a minute. I went as an American Sign Language interpreter. I went early for the sound check just to make sure I knew where to stand and so on. That's when I saw him. He was one of the performers in the front. When they all started singing, *he* had everyone's attention. With an ongoing confidence, he was drawing all the attention with his voice.

"The lead singer, a woman who had recorded several albums said, 'You are a very talented singer. *Solo* singer. If you don't know how to be a *backup* singer, I'll have to fire you. I don't have time to train you.' He started singing a lot closer to his heart and a lot further from her range." Jocelyn chuckled.

"Someone moved me further from the all the singers, but I was alright with that. In thirty minutes, the Christmas concert would begin. That's when I realized the backup singer was a guy named Adam. We had several classes together. I hadn't recognized him because he'd changed his haircut.

"After sound check, I noticed my interpreting partner hadn't shown up yet. I was going to have to interpret the whole program myself. While I was thinking about this, Adam came over. He tried to say hello, but I didn't have time. I would only have a short break before I had to be up stage again for when people came in since there was no one but me to interpret.

"When we returned to get to our positions before the show, people were starting to enter. Most of the singers were sitting in the front row ready to move to their positions. There was no sign of Adam."

"Where were you?" asked Dahlia.

"I went on stage to interpret, but I kept worrying about where Adam was. And then I wondered why I was so worried about him. He was already going to be late."

Dahlia stopped me there. "Why were you so worried about him? He wasn't anyone important to you."

"I guess I had always thought there might be a spark of romantic interest between us. Maybe that was it. But that night I saw he was like a broken little boy who was always getting into trouble. I could see it before it happened." Jocelyn said.

"What happened?" Dahlia leaned forward.

"When each choir member arrived, they were early enough to walk through the back door. Adam, late, carried himself up the front stairs to the stage and nearly fell over the main minister. He stood right behind and below the Christmas tree. The main singer called the rest of the group to stand together and begin.

"In a minute, the tree near Adam made a sound like it tooted, making the audience laugh. I looked, but it was over. I couldn't imagine what he had done. While I watched, he held the branch and pulled on it like a mischievous boy, helping the tree make a silly sound."

"So, what did you learn from this one?" Dahlia asked.

"Anyone that makes me worry like a mommy within eight minutes of seeing him isn't the one for me."

#Click#

Chapter 5

THE YELLOW BUG

They met at a universal spiritual center. Both Jocelyn and Jeff were taking evening classes to learn how to live an authentic and meaningful life. They noticed each other immediately.

Jocelyn noticed his gentleness and humor. He was a John Denver lookalike. They shared a quick wit, and often their interchanges were an entertaining distraction for the class until the teacher reeled them in.

After class one night, Jeff lingered and mentioned to Jocelyn that the author of a book they were studying was speaking at a local venue. "Do you want to go?"

Jocelyn hesitated, not sure what to answer. What were Jeff's expectations? She wasn't sure she was ready to date yet, and she hadn't thought about dating Jeff. She was just now gaining a tentative foothold on her life. The spiritual center was a wonderful place to discover how to regain her equilibrium while also making new friends. Until now, that's how she thought of him—a wonderful new friend.

While considering turning down the invitation because she didn't want to do anything to spoil their fun connection, she wanted to hear this author.

Jeff put his hand on her arm. "I know you just went through a painful divorce. I just enjoy your company and thought it was something you might like to attend. Nothing more." He smiled.

Jocelyn smiled back. She could trust Jeff implicitly. He never said an unkind word to anyone. He was genuine and as sweet as any man could be. He had all the qualities of a great friend. Perhaps she should explore what else might be possible for their growing closeness.

He picked her up at her house in a yellow Volkswagen Bug. Jocelyn didn't even know those still existed. But it was immaculate, inside and out. The Bug was a comfortable ride. Jeff drove the way he lived, carefully and conscientiously.

They made fun conversation on the way. Jeff started doing an imitation of their current teacher. He'd put his glasses on, then perch them on his head. After seconds passed, he'd put a set of reading glasses on his nose sporting both pairs of glasses. With a quick nod, he'd drop the glasses from his head back to his nose the way the teacher did, wearing both pairs of glasses on his nose while he looked all over... for his glasses. It was hysterical, and Jocelyn laughed so hard she nearly peed in her pants.

Then, it was her turn. She poked a bit of fun of one of the women students who had a proper British accent. This woman was quite long winded but never really said anything. She seemed to always argue both sides of an argument, vacillating indecisively yet never coming to any conclusion.

"It seems to me," Jocelyn began with her best English accent, "if we consider the larger picture, we lose the very awareness of those things right before us. Yet if we take too much time and attention on the little things, we never understand the Gestalt of it all."

Jeff guffawed until he got the hiccups. Jocelyn snorted loudly, which, of course, sent Jeff into another fit of laughter, increasing the frequency and intensity of the hiccups. They had to pull the car over.

After the hysterics wound down, they embraced. Jeff hiccupped, and they started laughing all over again.

Once at the venue, they noticed the others seemed a rather mature and serious-minded crowd. Jeff and Jocelyn found their seats and tried to keep their giggles to themselves.

When the speaker began, the sound system would cut out about every third word. The author also had a thick Hispanic accent. Combined, these two things made it nearly impossible to understand the talk.

Jeff passed notes to Jocelyn with his best guess at what was being said or a funnier version of the topic. She would write back and expand upon the commentary with her take on it or her best joke about the situation. The notes became more and more fanciful and were too funny to contain their giddy happiness. They were like two kids in church, bursting at the seams trying not to giggle.

To cover the fact they were passing notes, Jeff would put his hand on Jocelyn's hand. Like the sound system, her heart would skip every third beat. She felt surprisingly close to him. It was as if they were the only two in the room, and the speaker and audience just provided a backdrop for their own private party.

After the third person shushed them, they decided to leave. They weren't getting much from the speaker, and they really just wanted to spend some unrestricted time together.

They decided to get a frozen yogurt. They looked at each other with a dare. Who could fit the most in their small cup? Jeff piled his high with samplings of every one of the twenty toppings.

When they got to the register, they tried to guess how much it all weighed. They wagered that whoever guessed the closest to the actual weight would be treated by the loser to their frozen yogurt prize. They were amazed they had exceeded a full pound of delectable treats in those little cups. In the end, Jeff forked over a whopping $14.00 to the cashier, who informed them this was a record breaker.

"It was worth it," Jeff said as they both enjoyed the yogurt. "I've never seen you so jubilant as you've been this whole evening." He touched her hand. "You're coming into your own, and I'm happy I could witness and enjoy your healing."

They ended the evening with a total sugar high and returned to the womb of the little, yellow Bug. As they drove back, Jeff shared more about himself. He talked about when he first found the spiritual center and how much it meant to him now.

"It's a wonderful place to focus on what's really important," he said. "To find out who you are and connect with people in a truly authentic way."

Jocelyn surprised herself as she reached over and put her hand on his. "I'm certainly enjoying our connection, Jeff."

He looked at her and smiled. "I'm so glad. I feel like we've known each other for a long time. That's how it was when I first met my partner at the center. It's so great to meet like-minded people. It's gratifying to belong to such a loving community."

She slowly pulled her hand back and placed it on her own lap. She looked out the window for a few moments. It was the first time there was silence between them since they met.

She finally turned to him. "Yes, it's good to have honest, authentic communication. It's so rare these days. In that vein, I just want to clarify something you just said. When you said 'partner,' did you mean you're gay?"

Jeff looked at her. "Yes. I thought you'd know that the minute you saw how clean I keep the car." He chuckled. "I'm really sorry if I mislead you in any way. I just really love your spirit and how much fun we have together. I hope that won't change."

Jocelyn tried to release any disappointment she was feeling. "Nope. Of course, that won't change. But I guess what they say is actually true. All the good ones are either taken or gay!"

#Click#

Chapter 6

OVERHAUL

That year to herself had been a gift. For the first time in her life, she had begun to know who she was and what she wanted. But now, her counselor and her friends were pushing her to start dating. At nearly sixty, she wasn't old, but she wasn't getting younger either.

One day she was visiting Dahlia, who brought two cups of tea to the dining room table.

"Jocelyn, let me be frank. You're already receiving AARP magazines. If you don't start dating soon, you're going to end up with a cat, then another and another! You have to get out there and start meeting men."

"It's been so long since I was 'out there,' if it's not in my new GPS, I'll never find it."

"Hey," Dahlia said excitedly, "I know a great guy who would be perfect for you. Tom is an intelligent, mature gentleman who is emotionally healthy and financially stable."

While Jocelyn experienced some trepidation about leaving the safety of her womb-like woman cave, she trusted Dahlia with her life, and he did sound promising.

The date was arranged for the following Friday evening. Now Jocelyn had to ask herself, was this a come as you are event or one requiring a camouflage campaign? As she looked in the mirror, her comfortable self looked back. They were both surprised at how much gray hair had permeated the top of her head and had pushed down the honey-blond color she had abandoned. Without number 68, that's exactly how old she looked. She didn't mind looking her age, even when she actually felt much younger, but this sixty-eight-year-old gray-haired woman in the bathroom mirror had to go.

Wait a minute. Why was it when a man in our culture showed gray, he was considered mature, attractive, and distinguished? We use words like *salt-and-pepper* or *flecked with gray*. But when a woman is gray, she is simply old. What was to be done about this obvious double standard? She had only three days to decide just who was going to show up for this date!

She asked herself how *she* wanted to look. What would make *her* feel good? After visiting in the mirror a bit longer, she called for an appointment.

For most women, getting ready for a date often requires an entire regimen, not unlike a complete home renovation. There was much to be refurbished, revamped, removed, patched up and painted over. A restoration like Jocelyn's began with a visit to the salon to show the world how youthful she felt. She told herself this was a chance for a do over with her hair and her life.

For the past year, Jocelyn took daily dance and yoga classes as a way to cope with the divorce. In the beginning, she couldn't eat or sleep from the depression, so exercise did her a world of good. Her comfortable self lived in the same stretchy yoga pants day in and day out. Now as she tried on a few items from her closet, she was shocked to realize she had lost nearly fifty pounds! All her clothes hung on her like big burlap sacks.

She invited Dahlia to go shopping. They spent a fun afternoon trying on the latest styles that all looked sensational on Jocelyn. She didn't even recognize the figure in the mirror.

"Depression really agrees with me!" she said with a laugh.

Dahlia helped her pick a few mixed and matched pieces that would be perfect for the date with Tom and other fun events.

"Do you want to go to the cosmetic counter and try a free makeover?" Dahlia asked while pulling Jocelyn's arm in that direction.

Again, Jocelyn thought about how only the women were expected to cover over all signs of having been alive. While being dragged by her friend, she asked, "Why is it that the lines by a man's eyes are called smile lines and ours are called crow's feet? Why are we expected to cover our age spots but it's a natural sign of maturity for men? Other than helping the economy by fueling a pervasive mass retail marketplace, why are women expected to spend so much money to cover their true appearance?"

"Okay," Dahlia sighed. "I know where this is leading, and it's definitely not the cosmetic counter. I can't argue with you, and I certainly want to encourage you to be true to yourself."

They went out to lunch instead.

Jocelyn hadn't wanted to ask. She didn't want to seem shallow. But after spending nearly an entire day shopping and prepping, she felt she had the right to know.

"So, Dahlia." She tried to sound nonchalant. "What does he look like?"

Dahlia's eyes widened as she looked up from behind a giant sandwich creating a mustache of lettuce, tomato, and a wheat roll. There was a dab of mayonnaise dangling on her chin like a small goatee.

"Who?" Dahlia managed to ask through a large mouthful of everything.

"Tom! The man of the hour! Your choice for my impending escort, 'the perfect man' for me. What does he look like?"

"Nice. He looks nice."

Jocelyn tried to hide her impatience with this wom-wich (part woman, mostly sandwich). "What I want to know is… does he look like my next big regret? Blunder? Or major life slipup?"

Dahlia put her sandwich down and even wiped off her chin. "Oh! You're nervous about the date. Completely understandable. But rest assured, Tom is the complete package. He's really nice, mature, intelligent, and a known entity. We've been friends for years. It's not like you booted up your computer and selected a work of fiction from one of those online meat markets. He's a real person. He's sweet and authentic. What does he look like? He looks like a man who's a little lost and lonely. He looks a lot like you."

Jocelyn smiled weakly. Dahlia was right. She did feel a little lost and somewhat lonely at times. Even though she didn't learn a single physical attribute in that answer, she felt calmed by his description.

When Friday arrived, she set out to meet Tom at a restaurant he'd selected. He was seated outside. When Jocelyn arrived, he stood to greet her. After the initial hello, they went inside and ordered a variety of tapas and pastries.

"I thought you might like this place. It's unique, the food is great, and we can sit outside, if you like."

They took their full plates outside and sat comfortably on the brightly colored outdoor furniture. Tom got up to move an umbrella to ensure Jocelyn was protected from the hot afternoon sun. He was an old-fashioned gentleman.

"My friend, Dahlia, speaks very highly of you," she began. "But I don't really know much about you. What do you do when you're not partaking of tapas?"

"I'm recently retired. I was an attorney in private litigation and trial law, including criminal and civil cases. But, now, my mother is aging, so I left my practice to help her."

She thought he was nice, just as Dahlia had portrayed him. Jocelyn had worked in the court setting so they had lots of war stories to share.

As he talked though, she felt an unfamiliar tugging and ache. It was as if her feelings were shutting down. She was interested in what he was saying, but she seemed to be uncontrollably floating farther and farther away from him with her own thoughts drowning him out.

She was surprised to realize the feelings that were surfacing were the hurt from her ex-husband's unexpected departure exactly a year ago. It seemed to have left her with a thick scar around her heart, holding it tightly, preventing it from inviting anyone else in. As she watched this nice man's lips moving, a loud voice inside her head was shouting at her to be cautious.

She had never mistrusted before. And certainly, this nice man had done nothing to deserve this large helping of it. She tried to refocus on what he was saying.

After the date, she made an appointment with her counselor, Deborah, to see what this was about.

Her counselor smiled empathetically. "You did a great job of getting out there for the first time. You overhauled your hair, your clothes, and your attitude about dating. Now, it's time to look a bit more into the best ways for you to get past the feelings of betrayal you experienced when your marriage ended. It's far reaching to be so loving and trusting for thirty-five years, only to be left so abruptly. Jocelyn, you have healed in so many ways. Now, it's time to learn to trust again. To risk being hurt, knowing you are far more prepared to deal with it."

"So, you're saying my 'overhaul' is not complete? I thought once the year was done, I'd be ready to move on with my life. How long does it take to fix a broken heart?"

"It's different for everyone," her counselor told her. "Your circumstances make it exceptionally difficult to accept. You were happy in your marriage and didn't anticipate it ending abruptly. In many ways, as we've talked about before, you suffered a death. Of your marriage. Of your spouse. Only this was worse. Worse, because you couldn't participate in the decision and didn't even know the reason until months later. When you think about Alex now, what do you feel?"

Jocelyn began to cry. After a year, she thought she had cried out every last tear. But what Deborah said resonated deeply. "I'm really pissed."

"I've been waiting for you to get there. Tell me about it."

"I feel like he wasted the best years of my life. He stole my youth. He didn't want to have children, and now it's too late for me. I'm at the stage in life where I should be able to relax and enjoy my life, travel, be counting grandchildren like the rest of my friends. Instead, I'm alone.

"I'm doing better with it, but I don't deserve to end up alone. I supported him through hard times, through years of him being unemployed. And instead of feeling supported and loved in return, I am abandoned, left fending for myself. Alone."

"You're finally angry. Most women I see start there. It took you a year. I'm proud of your progress. Anger, while uncomfortable, is a much more powerful feeling than sadness. Use that power to keep the movement going."

"Going where? What's next?" Jocelyn asked.

"You keep going out. And we keep going in, deeper."

Jocelyn wished she could go back to that cosmetic department with Dahlia and apply a thick layer of makeup to cover over all that had happened. She'd paint a big smile on her face, call Tom, and get on with her new life.

But she knew her therapist was right. She nodded to Deborah. "I've made it this far. Now, it's time to overhaul my heart."

Deborah gave her a hug as she left. "Don't worry. You're doing everything you need to do. With your great friends as a support system and your willingness to do what's needed, you'll get through this. You just may be surprised at how much more you enjoy your new life."

Jocelyn made her way to her car. Alright then. No fake smile. No more tears. One step at a time towards a happy, whole, fearless new her.

#Click#

Chapter 7

THE ESCAPE VEHICLE

Barb was one of Jocelyn's oldest friends. They were both born the same year. Her divorce preceded Jocelyn's by five years. She was Mutt to Jocelyn's Jeff as she towered over Jocelyn's five-foot-two stature by nearly a foot. It was one of the reasons Jocelyn always said she "looked up to Barb."

She brought a special gift to Jocelyn's home. As she burst through the door, she shouted. "Happy Divorcée Day, girlfriend!"

A few other friends joined them, and they had a small Clicking for Mr. Right party to set up an online dating profile for her.

Barb plopped down on the couch and opened her laptop, showing a profile from an online dating site.

When Jocelyn noticed it was a woman's profile she laughed. "I'm not giving up on men, yet."

"Come here; look more closely." She patted the couch next to her as her eyebrows raised high on her forehead.

Jocelyn rolled her eyes but complied like a puppy hoping for a treat. As she looked at the page, she was shocked. "Hey, that's me! How did you get five photos of me looking so good? Did you Photoshop these?"

"Didn't have to. You're beautiful. Now, I won't be the only one to know it."

Jocelyn read the text Barb had written. She was a poet, and this was as close to poetry as dating profiles come.

Make yourself known to me. I trust there's a reason it took this long for us to meet. I know I will recognize you immediately. You and I together are: intelligent, kind, loving, emotionally secure, financially stable, spiritually curious, and ready to partake in life deeply. We will balance traveling adventures with a peaceful, loving home life. It matters little where we are or what we do. It's fun and meaningful… because we do it together. We are a soft place to land for one another, always having each other's back with a love that is authentic, deep, and ever growing. Make yourself known to me…

"Of course, you can change anything you like. I just wanted to get you started. In fact, I paid for the first three months. After that you're on your own."

"Why would I need it for three months? Aren't these guys available and looking for a partner? I'm only looking for one. In three months, I should be able to find us both soulmates, right?"

"I'm not sure it's that easy. If anyone can, it would be you."

They shared a bottle of champagne and laughed their way through the process. Jocelyn started having fun and even took profile pics provocatively exposing her shoulder or leaning backwards over the patio railing with a huge bottle of champagne to her mouth. Of course, she had no intention of uploading these "party animal" pictures.

Her slightly tipsy girlfriends at the coming out or coming on…line party revealed several dating horror stories. She learned there were a plethora of players and inappropriate people to meet. At her age, she didn't have the desire for such things, nor the time.

"Now to stay safe you will need to be armed with a bit of important information."

"Such as?"

"For at least the first three dates, or longer until you feel comfortable, meet your date at the location. Drive your own escape vehicle. This prevents him from knowing your address too soon and allows you freedom of movement. You'll be able to extricate yourself in case the gentleman is no gentleman."

"Sounds like good advice. What else?"

"Never go to his home alone until you absolutely know and trust him. And don't invite him to your home, either, until he's earned your trust. Something happens to a man's brain, or another organ overriding the brain, when entering a building with a bed. In fact, never go to an isolated or dark place without other people around. Literally stay in the light, among other people within earshot."

"Jeez, this sounds dangerous."

"Learn from others' mistakes. I'm not saying all men are dangerous. But anyone can write a work of fiction and post phony or old pictures on these sites, and a few precautions can go a long way in protecting yourself."

"What else?"

"Ah, the student is eager. This is good, Grasshopper. Look for red flags."

"Such as?"

"Things that indicate he's a player, an ex-con, or married and using the dating sites as an extracurricular hobby."

"Okay, Dating Guru, any more wisdom and I'll be afraid to start clicking."

"That's good for now. When you start setting up dates, text me his full name and where you'll be."

"Yes, Mother." Jocelyn laughed.

"Laugh if you want, but you are too precious to me to have anything happen to you. You deserve happiness and to be safe while looking for it."

Jocelyn hugged Barb. "Thanks for being such a wonderful friend. Since you found your wonderful significant other on this site, I will follow your tutelage."

She was making every effort to use the online filtering system to select men who demonstrated values and integrity. She found a rather attractive looking gent who fit the bill. He had a handsome, sculpted face with thick, black hair and dark, penetrating eyes. He was a widower.

Nervously, she wrote him. She was so surprised when John responded immediately to her note.

He asked her out for a date and offered to pick her up. She thought about this as he seemed extremely kind. But Barb had repeatedly expressed concerns about going in a car with a virtual (and digital) stranger.

They agreed to meet at a beachfront restaurant. When she arrived, he was already there, seated at an ocean-front table on a bustling outdoor patio. They were both relieved, as the photos on their profiles actually did represent their appearance.

After the introductory icebreakers, Jocelyn said, "So it must have been so difficult to lose your wife that way."

He seemed to stiffen and said in a defensive tone, "I was acquitted of all charges by a jury of my peers."

"Oh." Jocelyn was taken aback. "What charges?" She tried to sound calm.

"Murder. I did *find* her, but I never *pushed* her."

"I'm sorry. Did she fall from a high place?" She was not able to stop the shaking in her voice.

His voice was without emotion, like well-practiced witness testimony. "I had built a third story deck. I hadn't gotten around to putting up the railing yet. I guess I shouldn't have put that off for three months, as I knew she had a drinking problem."

Jocelyn was uncomfortable taking this further, so she asked in a lighter tone. "So have you been dating since?"

"Yes, but I was acquitted of those charges too."

"Murder?" Jocelyn suddenly wanted to be anywhere else.

He laughed. "Oh, no. She just accused me of beating her."

Jocelyn couldn't sit there for another moment. She glanced at her phone as if it had just vibrated. "Oh, John, I'm so sorry, but I just realized I have a meeting now. Got my dates all wrong" *Got THIS date all wrong.*

Angering a bit, he said, "So you don't want to meet again?"

"Oh, I'd love to." She tried to sound sincere. "I just have to go right now."

"Can I at least walk you to your car?" His face reddened.

"Oh, sure. I'd like that." She really didn't want to anger this man since it was obvious he had exceptional legal representation. He paid the bill, and she led him across the street to a large parking lot.

She stopped at a red sports car. "Well, this is me. Thank you so much for making time to meet with me." She extended her hand, and he shook it. She practiced in her head how to break away from a wrist hold by turning her arm toward the thumb of the intruder.

Luckily, he released her hand easily, and she watched him walk away. When he was a safe distance away, she ducked down near that red car. Then she ducked between cars and crossed the street to where her escape vehicle was actually parked.

She was very glad he didn't have her address. She vowed to always follow the escape vehicle rule until she learned more about future dates… if she would ever partake of another.

#Click#

Chapter 8

SUNDAY TIMES

Now, like dealing with most things in her life, Jocelyn kept an open mind and a positive attitude. After that murderer fiasco, she decided to sign up for an exclusive dating service that promised to screen men carefully. Well, at least they did eliminate financially irresponsible men, those whose checks to them had bounced.

Even for an avid online shopping guru like Jocelyn, "shopping" for a life partner on the internet was nothing short of bizarre. It made her feel like a dog chasing his tail. This one had no pictures? *Click.* That one didn't dance? *Click.* This one was too tall? *Click.* That one didn't like dogs? *Click!* Even as exhaustion and disappointment set in, she was convinced that her soulmate was just one mere mouse click away. *Click. Click. Click.*

So, with her divorced sister, Barb, and Dahlia as her expert dating support team, she bravely continued with the emails, phone calls, and then—the most fear inducing of them all—the first date.

This particular encounter was to be an innocuous meeting for breakfast at a local café. They had planned to meet on Sunday morning for a bite to eat, then go for a walk on the beach. Rule number two (learned on this date): Only plan one activity so there is a finite commitment with a graceful way to exit with everyone's self-esteem intact.

Jocelyn arrived on time and arranged to be seated toward the back of the restaurant near a window. This gave her the vantage point of watching for his arrival and the consequent approach. It also gave her access to the back door and the parking lot.

About ten minutes later, he approached. She did recognize him from his picture, a good thing—unlike another guy whose picture was older than her nine-year-old dog or the one before him who used his brother's picture. As he got closer, she could see he had something in his hands. No, it wasn't a bouquet of flowers or a box of candy. It was the Sunday newspaper.

She decided right then if he dug out the sports page while they ate, she'd simply get up and leave.

He didn't even wait for the food. Didn't seem to want to waste time saying more than hello and promptly dug out the sports section and dangled the front page in front of Jocelyn. She didn't move a muscle. It hung there between them like a dark cloud, and then it began to shake. "Oh," he said, and he placed the two sections on the side of the table.

She wasn't sure if he thought they could just pick up where he and his ex-wife left off without skipping a beat or going through all that messy "getting to know you" stuff that comes with a new relationship. She would have left right then but was enjoying the delicious, fresh-squeezed orange juice. Based on the crowd that was forming at the door, the food promised to be equally satisfying.

They suffered through an excruciating exchange where the need to add political affiliation to the list of required fields on the online dating site became apparent. The whole experience made her wish she had just accepted the newspaper. Ironically, he called her several times wanting a second date.

This brought her to rule number three: If you don't like them at all, they will call and call. If you are at all attracted to them, you will never hear from them again. Not sure why this happens, but a synopsis of what is happening out there is that he likes her, but she likes that other guy, but he's more attracted to that one, who has her eye on this other one.

But Jocelyn was an eternal optimist. She'd either endure the process to find her true soul mate or would learn to love herself better in the process. Or both.

#Click#

Chapter 9

In a Family Way

Jocelyn felt like she was fifteen again as she prepared for another date from an online dating site. She looked in the mirror and fully expected to see braces and a face full of pimples. She'd been trying hard to find a perk to being fifty-eight and suddenly thrust back into the single world. She finally found it: no pimples. Although it was not comforting enough to dissuade all the anxiety churning her stomach.

Having found each other online at CatchYourMatch. com, they agreed to meet on the pier. This would come in handy, if after meeting, she wanted to throw this catch back. She chuckled at the thought and was pleased to see her sense of humor was still intact. She had her doubts that such a long-time wife could transform herself into a charming first date.

When she arrived at the beach, she was actually hoping she couldn't find a parking space so she'd have a legitimate excuse to turn the car around and go home. There were never any parking spaces at the beach this time of year. Thousands of tourists invaded all the beaches in San Diego.

To guarantee she'd have a great excuse to leave for lack of parking, she drove right to the water's edge. Just as the ocean came into sight, a car in front of her put on its backup lights and created a parking space people would die for. And now, she did want to die. She pulled into this highly desirable waterfront property and turned off the engine.

The pier reached out before her like an invitation. Crossing over the threshold from solid ground to wooden planks hovering questionably over the crashing waves seemed the appropriate venue for this entrance into her new, tenuous single life.

She plodded toward the line of demarcation between being on familiar ground and her next life assignment to "walk the dating plank."

Just then, a man who looked like her date's profile picture came at her at nearly a run, with a huge sunflower in his hand. He was smiling wide, and his gait was so enthusiastic she thought he'd crash right into her. Before she knew it, she was face to face with that big sunflower.

Normally, these were her favorites. But this one seemed to be challenging her to a duel. She forced a smile and pulled the flower down from her face.

"Thank you so much." She was secretly cursing the fact that she was going to have to carry this huge bud around like a flag that announced, "This middle-aged woman is on a date."

Ironically, and to make matters worse, her date's name was Bud.

They walked the length of the pier and actually had a pleasant conversation. He was very devoted to his family, and that was something Jocelyn liked. She never had the opportunity to have children, so the thought of becoming part of a family in a nurturing role appealed to her.

"My daughter, Sara, and I are close," he explained. "She has a spitfire of a little boy, my grandson, Joey." He paused and then went on. She's now pregnant with my granddaughter." As he spoke of this he seemed to sadden. His eyes cast downward.

Jocelyn touched his arm. "Is there something wrong?"

"Oh, I don't want to burden you with this." He looked out at the ocean to regain his composure.

"I would appreciate if you would share. It wouldn't be a burden but a way we can know each other honestly."

He turned to look her in the eyes. "There's a problem with the baby. The doctors say there's nothing they can do. Even if she makes it to term, she will die shortly after being born. They recommend Sara terminate the pregnancy. We're trying to figure out what to do."

"I'm so sorry." Jocelyn said, and she was. She could see how painful this was for this man who already loved his granddaughter. "If there's any way I can be of support, please let me know. Even if it's just to talk."

"Thank you, Jocelyn. That's kind of you. I think we all need to talk about it, especially Sara. I wonder if you wouldn't mind meeting her. I think she'd really like to get another woman's perspective."

"I'd be happy to spend time with her," Jocelyn responded easily. "I wouldn't mind meeting Mr. Spitfire too."

Bud smiled. "Good idea. Let's make it a family dinner so you can meet my mother, Sara, Joey, and of course, I'll get to see you again too."

Jocelyn wasn't experienced with how dating was supposed to go. She was pretty sure meeting the whole family on the second date was unusual. But she could see how much pain Bud was experiencing. She wanted to help.

They parted, and she returned to her prize-winning parking spot. She got in the car but didn't turn it on. She rolled down the window, listened to and watched the ocean's whitecapped waves. The sound of the ocean reminded her that all of life has a rhythm and with the divorce, she had lost her own.

The waves know the exact right time to come in to shore. She hoped it was her time to learn the next direction her life might take. She didn't know how she felt about Bud, but she had survived her re-entry into being single. She could see new possibilities forming. What would it be like to be someone's mother, helping her through such difficult life choices? She yearned to receive love, but even more so, to give it with a newly opened heart.

When it was time to go to the family dinner at Bud's house, she was grateful for being invited into their home and lives. When she knocked on the door, she heard light footsteps running to greet her.

It was the "little spitfire." Joey swung open the front door and yelled, "She's here!" He looked up at Jocelyn and said in rapid succession, "Wanna see my room? I have two dogs you can play with. I can show you the backyard.

I have a tent in my room, and you can go in with me. Do you want to?"

Bud came to greet her, smiling about Joey's exuberant barrage. "Let Jocelyn come in and say hello to everyone, then you can show her your room. Okay, little buddy?"

"Okay. I'll go in my room and hide. You come find me!" He ran full force in socked feet and slid down the hall, coming to a stop at the opening of his bedroom.

Bud and Jocelyn laughed. "You have about three minutes until he shows up again, so let me introduce you to the rest of the family."

They walked into the kitchen where Jocelyn met Bud's mother, Margaret. She was in her nineties. Bud had shared with Jocelyn that Margaret was in the beginning stages of Alzheimer's.

Then they went into the dining room where Sara was setting the table. Sara was sweet and looked more like eighteen than her actual age of twenty-six. She certainly seemed too young to have two children. She was around five feet seven inches with fair skin and very thin, light brown hair that reached down her back. She seemed so vulnerable and strong all at the same time. Jocelyn offered to help.

During dinner, Margaret sat on one side of Jocelyn and Joey claimed the seat on her other side. At one point in the meal, Margaret reached over with her hand and took some rice off Jocelyn's plate.

"Ma!" Bud yelled loudly, startling Jocelyn. "Don't do that! You already have rice on your plate. Don't take food from Jocelyn's plate, for crying out loud!"

"It's alright," Jocelyn said in a quiet voice, hoping to deescalate Bud's reaction about ninety percent. "There's plenty more, and I don't mind sharing with my new friend, Margaret."

"See! She doesn't mind," Margaret shrieked at Bud.

Hmmm, guess the apple didn't fall far from this tree.

Joey chimed in. "Granny, you can have my aspa-guses, I want to share too!"

Sara told Joey in a quiet voice, "It's so nice you offered to share, but you need to eat all of your vegetables, including the as-par-ag-us."

After dinner, Bud offered to clean up so Sara and Jocelyn could have a private visit. They went into a back bedroom where it was quiet.

"Did Dad tell you about my little girl?" She gently rubbed the little bump that was her stomach.

"Yes," Jocelyn responded gently. "How are you doing?"

"Well," Sara began. "They all want me to terminate the pregnancy. They say

there's no chance of her surviving. I'm just so confused. I don't know what to do."

"Sara, it's your baby and your decision. What is it YOU want to do?"

"No one has even asked me that. The doctors, my Dad, my friends all just tell me what to do. You're the first one to even ask what I want."

Jocelyn sat quietly to give her time to think.

"The way I see it" — Sara sat straight up and seemed to gain inner strength— "God gave me this baby for a reason.

She's with me so I can take care of her. Even if I give birth and she dies within minutes, I think I'm supposed to give her the chance to live. Life is no less important because it's short. I want to take care of her until God decides to take her."

Jocelyn smiled at Sara. "You seem very clear. Sara, there's no right or wrong way to do this. This is your child, so it should be your decision. Listen to your strong heart and follow your faith."

"Thank you for saying that. The baby's father and I really want to keep her as long as we can. My father is worried it would be too hard on me to give birth and watch her die. But I can handle it, if that's what happens. I have to."

Jocelyn stroked her hair. "You're very strong. If I can help along the way, please let me know."

"I'd like to talk with you from time to time. It helps a lot. Thank you so much."

Sara reached for Jocelyn, and they hugged. "Of course. I will be here for you, honey."

Just then, Joey burst into the room, gliding his socks over tile toward Jocelyn as if he were sliding into home plate. "Wanna come into my room now?" he shouted up at her.

Sara gave Jocelyn a nod as she wiped a small tear from the corner of her eye.

"I'd love to," Jocelyn told him. "Lead the way."

She was playing with blocks inside the very small tent with Joey when Bud came in to rescue her. All in all, it was a lovely visit.

Bud and Jocelyn saw each other a few more times, although she spoke with Sara by phone more frequently.

Three months later, Bud called Jocelyn. "It's time. Can you meet us at the hospital?"

"Yes. I'm on my way."

The baby was born, and the tiny girl was swaddled in a blanket and passed from one family member to another. Each person had a few precious moments with her. She was hugged and kissed with soft words of love and prayers. When she was handed back to Sara, the baby had taken on a bluish hue. The nurse said it wouldn't be much longer.

Sara spoke to her. "I thank God that we got to meet you, my little one. I love you with my full heart and will do so for the rest of my days. You're such a gift to me, my darling. We all love you."

Sara held the swaddled infant long after she had passed. The nurse told Sara when she was ready to place the child in the bassinet and the nurse would come back for her.

The hospital gave Sara a special teddy bear that was weighted to feel more like a baby. This was for new mothers who had lost their baby so they wouldn't leave empty handed. While the intention of this program was sincere, it fell far short of anything resembling a healing solution.

Shortly after, Jocelyn went to the funeral for the baby girl. She sat with the family to give them support, but her own heart was breaking as the hearse drove up. A man opened the back of the long, black vehicle and took out a small, three-foot long, white box with pink flowers on top. It took her a moment to realize this little box was a coffin holding that precious little baby. It was nearly too much to bear. They carefully placed the small package into the reopened gravesite of a family member so she wouldn't be alone.

Jocelyn put her arm around Sara, expecting to hold her up. But Sara was sitting tall and strong with what looked like a loving smile on her face. Sara's faith provided assurance that her baby had come home to God's loving hands.

Jocelyn realized how deeply she loved Sara. She was the closest thing to a daughter she'd ever experienced. Their connection was even more beautiful and rewarding than she'd imagined.

She also had a strong heart connection to Joey and Margaret.

But for all the love she felt for this family, unfortunately she hadn't fallen in love with Bud. As hard as she tried, she simply didn't have feelings for him. It would have been wonderful if it had happened, but she owed herself the chance at a true and lasting love. As difficult as it was, she said goodbye to this first new life she'd tried on. At least now she knew the world was full of possibilities for this ex-Sadie, Sadie, long married lady.

#Click#

Chapter 10

THREE'S A CROWD

Jocelyn was feeling desperately alone in the evenings. She hadn't lived by herself, without college roommates or her husband in over forty years. The house was different now. The silence was painful and so quiet, except for the echoes of conversations past.

That couch was where he told her he was leaving. That door was the portal to his freedom and her entrance into this hellish nightmare. Too many horrid memories in each corner of that building that used to be their home together.

When she was working or shopping or otherwise around people, she was fine. She'd conduct board meetings at the office. She'd communicate with customers all day. She managed the whole staff. Negotiated new contracts with vendors. She felt fine, as long as she was among the living.

Until she headed home. To that large, empty shell that now contained the remnants of her personal life. The anxiety would come in waves. It would punch her in the solar plexus, from inside the depths of her stomach. It was like nothing she'd ever experienced before. It happened as soon as she left for "home."

She was determined to minimize these feelings by creating reasons to go out at night. Thanks to the internet, the most readily attainable activity was a steady stream of dates. In fact, she arranged a date every evening.

Of course, in addition to staying busy and around people, there was always a chance one of these meetings could lead to a long-term relationship. She always had hope.

One night she made a date with Samuel, suggested by a dating service she had contacted. From the description, he didn't seem at all what she was seeking. It was Saturday evening, and she didn't have any plans, so she accepted. They were to meet at her favorite Mexican restaurant. If nothing else, she'd manage to escape the torturous woman house for a few hours and enjoy a nice meal.

As she was getting ready to leave, she received a call from Tom, a man who had captured her interest on MatchMakers. com over the last few weeks. He'd been away on a business trip and called to meet for a drink that evening.

She'd never done this before, but she told him she would meet him at eight o'clock… at the same Mexican restaurant where she was meeting Samuel at six. She figured she'd have plenty of time since she wasn't really interested in Samuel and didn't have to drive between the two dates.

She headed for the restaurant. Samuel wasn't terribly attractive, but they shared several interests and their conversation was fun and engaging. So much so, that when she glanced at her phone, she was shocked to see it was eight o'clock.

"Oh my God!" She hoped she hadn't just said that out loud.

"What's wrong?" he asked.

She had. "Oh." She had to think fast. "I just realized I told my friend I'd meet her at eight at her place. She's having marital problems and needed an ear. I'm so sorry, but I have to run."

"That's fine. I hope we can do this again soon."

"I'd like that," she said, surprised at how much she meant it.

She started to wonder how to manage this. She race-walked toward the front of the restaurant, feeling like Cinderella when the clock struck twelve, praying one of her shoes didn't come flying off and that Tom hadn't arrived yet. She ducked into the restroom.

Her heart was racing. How could she have gotten herself into this position? Had Samuel left the table yet, gone out of the restaurant? Had Tom arrived? Were they both in the lobby right outside the door she was hiding behind?

"Hi" A voice from behind made her jump. "You coming or going?" It was a woman heading to the sink in the bathroom.

"Not really sure." Jocelyn couldn't begin to figure out how to explain why she was standing immobilized by the door.

"Oh. You have Montezuma's revenge? That happens if you're not used to Mexican food. Happens to me with Indian food."

That would do. Jocelyn nodded and went into one of the stalls until the woman left. Geez, she felt like Tom Cruise in *Mission Impossible,* and she almost got caught.

It had been twelve minutes of hiding, and she decided it was time to face the music. She opened the door slowly and peeked to where she and Samuel had been sitting. He was still there, with a cup of coffee and a piece of pie. She slipped quickly into the lobby and out of his line of sight to see if Tom was there. He wasn't.

Perhaps he'd come and left. She was actually hoping for that so she could leave. This was worse than being home. She walked out of the restaurant determined to get to her car before Samuel came out and saw her.

"There you are," she heard from behind her near the front door of the restaurant. "How did you get past me? I've been sitting here for at least ten minutes."

"Oh, Tom. Hi. I got here early so I went to the restroom to freshen up." Not a lie.

She needed to get Tom inside to the bar so they didn't cross paths with Samuel. "Shall we go to the bar for that drink?"

She never drank alcohol on dates, but she might make an exception tonight. She hurriedly ran him into the bar. Just as she sat down at a table, she spied Samuel leaving the restaurant. *Note to self, I am never doing this again.*

As soon as Tom started talking, she realized her second date was the opposite of the first. He was extremely good looking, yet everything he said was about how wonderful he thought himself to be. He was egotistical, bordering on narcissistic. He talked for nearly forty-five minutes without asking her a single thing about herself.

She was amazed how much her pre-judgements about each of them had been one hundred percent wrong. She also was surprised at herself. She had gone from being an "old married fart" to 007 in one night. And one night was enough.

She didn't like lying. Rarely did it in her civilian life. She especially didn't like hiding in bathrooms, or at all. She was definitely not a "player." She vowed to start facing her situation with more dignity and integrity from now on. She'd force herself to spend more time figuring out how to do this dating thing while remaining true to herself and more respectful of others.

Besides, after the charades and shenanigans of that evening, staying home alone seemed a far more attractive choice.

#Click#

Chapter 11

LOOKING FOR RED FLAGS

Jocelyn's quest to meet a new life partner was her way to turn life's lemons into lemonade… or hopefully margaritas. She had earned advanced degrees in psychology, now she could actually put them to good use. Jocelyn wanted to avoid inauthentic communication discussing superficial subjects with "Mr. Wrong."

Dahlia had told her that sometimes it took as many as three meetings for red flags to appear indicating this date wasn't a good match. Jocelyn was determined to streamline the process of discovering a man's true character on the first date.

She teased her friends. "Perhaps a prerequisite Myers-Briggs personality test and an IQ test thrown in for good measure."

Her friends laughed, and Barb said, "If you upload a link to these tests onto your online profile, you'd most likely be perceived as a tad high maintenance!"

She still was thinking, if only there were a way to detect what they're NOT saying in their profiles. She went out with several men over a period of weeks only to find this one had lied about his age, the "retired" one was actually unemployed, the handsome one had used his brother's photo, or the absolute worst, that recently widowed one was married to a woman who was very much alive.

Finally, she agreed to meet a man named Ted, or so his online profile said. His picture showed a tall, boyish looking man. His eyes were large and penetrating, as if he were either exceptionally profound or sad. She hoped for insightful. A full head of thick hair, unusual in her balding age group.

They met in the lobby of the Mexican restaurant. She was relieved he resembled his picture; this was a good start. There was quite a wait for a table, so they took a pager and went for a sunset stroll around the large pond next to the restaurant.

As they walked side by side on the dirt footpath that wrapped all around the pond, Ted asked her a few first date interview questions about herself. The typical and boring, such as: How long were you married? How many children do you have? How long have you been on this particular online dating site? Blah, blah, blah...

When she had yada, yada, yada to his blah, blah, blah, it was her turn. They had strolled to the other side of the water, furthest from the restaurant. She noticed the sun going down, reflecting lovely on the water. She stopped for a moment. If nothing else happened from this evening, at least the nature walk was enjoyable.

As she started walking again, she heard herself say, "Ted, I'm curious. What are three things you don't want me to know about you?" How would this impromptu psychological research project progress? At least the conversation would become more interesting.

He stopped and faced her with a grimace. "Are you sure you want me to tell you *that* on our first date?"

She was surprised he had things immediately come to mind. At that moment, she realized the *right* response was "If I don't want you to know, why would I tell you?"

"Yes." She looked right into those large eyes. "I think the first date is the perfect time to show each other exactly who we are. Best to start communication in an honest way. No hiding, no games."

"I'm not sure that is such a good idea." He protested.

Now, she was actually growing curious about what it could possibly be. "Well Ted, it's up to you. But starting out withholding parts of yourself makes it difficult for me to know you. Right?"

"Okay." He took in a very deep breath, as if getting ready to do an Olympic jump into new territory. He paused again while he looked to the pond as if he were contemplating diving in, as it was the only escape route now. "I… well it happened… I mean there was an occasion, well, actually, more like three or four times in which…" Ted paused, then said very quickly, like ripping off a bandage, "I inappropriately touched my daughter."

It took Jocelyn a moment to realize she'd stopped breathing. Then, she took a slow breath to recover while making sure her face didn't convey her inner shock. Now she was thinking about an escape route. Trying to make this somehow less horrifying, she asked, "You mean your *stepdaughter*?" Although she knew it would not lessen the crime or her response to it.

"No," he said hesitantly. "It was … my own daughter." He quickly added, "But she was sixteen, and *she* started it!"

"Oh." Jocelyn took a step back from him. She calculated the fastest way out was back the way they had come. She walked backward a few steps. "Ted, I know that was difficult for you, and I appreciate you sharing this."

His face reddened, and his voice rose. "That's not even why her mother divorced me."

Jocelyn was praying he didn't divulge any more. The red flags were so thick, she could no longer even see his face.

"You know," she told him in a very calm voice, "I just think it best if we part ways now. You and I are not going to work out. But I wish you luck." She turned and began walking back, picking up the pace a bit.

"Wait, I only told you *one* thing. You had asked me for three. Don't you want to hear the other two?"

"Not necessary. But thanks for the offer." She began race walking to her car. She was afraid to look back in case he was following her.

"I told you it was too soon to tell you!" he yelled to her back. "You insisted. Now you aren't even willing to get to know me. Am I supposed to keep paying for a few little mistakes the rest of my life?"

By then she had reached and settled into the comfortable confines of her locked escape vehicle with soft music playing on the radio. Other than being hungry, her world was intact. But she was aware now that this could have gone very differently.

She was beginning to realize finding a mate wasn't going to be a walk in the park. Not even with one with a lovely pond. Even in such a peaceful setting, she was going to have to be much more careful.

This kind of thing never happened in romantic comedies. Alec Baldwin would never have uttered those words to Meryl Streep. Even if "it is complicated."

With some modification, Jocelyn now had a method by which red flags would be run up the pole in a matter of moments. Of course, from now on, she planned to only ask about one event, rather than three. And she would ask on a pre-date phone call.

How would she have answered that question? She mused to herself. What would she not want a first date to know about her?

She was pondering her own red flags as she drove to a great new restaurant, relieved to be by herself. She couldn't think of a thing. Perhaps if she dated much longer, she would have one new secret to divulge: She considered writing a book about this whole crazy dating process.

#Click#

Chapter 12

THE WEDDING ESCORT

"What time would you like me to pick you up?" Eddie asked Jocelyn over the phone.

"Aren't I out of your way?"

He laughed. "You? You are never out of my way. You *are* my way."

Jocelyn was taken aback. Some women might have thought that was the most romantic thing a man could say. She saw it as a potential red flag but, she had vowed to give him the benefit of the doubt and try hard not to analyze every little thing.

The "date" they were planning was a bit complicated, and she'd started it by making an unusual request of him. "I'd like you to come to the wedding of my best friend's daughter. It's a destination wedding, so it involves a long drive and two nights in a hotel."

"I'd love that!" he'd replied without any hesitation and an alarming amount of enthusiasm.

"I just want to be clear about something." Jocelyn tried to calm him and his expectations down. "We've not yet been intimate, and the fact that we'll be staying in a hotel doesn't bring with it any guarantee that our relationship will suddenly be fast-forwarded. Whatever feels right for the both of us is what we will do. Understand and agree?"

"Yes. Sure. Whatever makes you comfortable," he promised.

She felt only a bit comforted as he still looked like the Cheshire cat, seemingly unable to stop smiling when they left for the trip.

Several of her friends encouraged her to bring him. They advised she just relax and have fun.

Even her ninety-two-year old mother said, "Now just go and let loose. Don't be you. Be fun. Go in that fancy hotel room and jump on the bed!"

"You mean jump *in* the bed?"

"In, on … do it all!" Her mom laughed.

As soon as she had invited him, she regretted it. She knew from experience that something happens to a man when you enter a building with a bed in it. All his blood rushes immediately away from his brain.

She had called the hotel and upgraded the room. Instead of a standard room housing only a bed, she got a one-bedroom suite. It had a living room, kitchenette, and bedroom. The living room had a sofa that was a pull-out bed, just in case things didn't go as her mother wished. Normally, she would have gotten two rooms. But since the wedding and a conference were being held there that weekend, they were totally booked.

The drive there was pleasant. They talked, listened to music, and sang. Neither of them could carry a tune, so Jocelyn turned up the music to drown them both out. He put on an all-sixties station, and they were transported back to Woodstock.

When they arrived, the accommodations were very nice and, to Jocelyn's relief, very spacious. The balcony overlooked the ocean and a swimming pool.

"I'd love to take a walk on the beach," he said. "Shall we?"

"Why don't you do that? I'm going to freshen up from the drive and take a rest."

"Oh. I wouldn't go without you. I won't leave you on our first trip together," he said adamantly. "We are going to see how it is to be together twenty-four hours a day."

"Please do go for a walk now. It calls for rain all weekend, and if you don't go now you may not have another chance. Besides, I really would like some time to myself after the long drive."

She handed him his jacket and opened the door. He obediently walked through. His head hanging so low she didn't know if he was trying to be funny or had actually transitioned into Eeyore.

Jocelyn lay down for a few minutes. She thought about the first time she walked into Eddie's home. How surprised she was to see all the pictures of her posted all over the place. There were photos of her presenting in the classroom, pictures of her interpreting dynamic meetings, using a knee wheeler to help her with a broken ankle, at her at women's meetings, even on dates...

She didn't even know where he had gotten all these remnants of her life. Jocelyn would have to ask him. Without him knowing about her, he seemed to have a lot taken from her life.

Just as she seemed to be falling asleep, Eddie came into the room. He'd only been out about ten minutes. She should have gotten two rooms or just come up herself.

Whenever they were with her friends, he wouldn't speak. They were impressed with how quiet he was. She was so looking forward to seeing them, but she couldn't do it without the quiet shadow close behind her.

The first night, she slept in the big bed and locked the bedroom. The second night, he slept in the big bed and kept the door open, and she slept in the little bed. She couldn't wait to get back to her own bedroom, with the whole house locked tight.

On the way home with him, she started talking about how she was not feeling like they were in step with each other. "I really loved time with you, and I really loved the time I had when I was alone." Jocelyn asked him if he liked to be alone.

"I really hate when I am alone. When I was married, I would do anything to keep my wife with me. She was easy cause I just had to give her beer after beer. She stayed on the couch, and she would be with me the whole day. All you woman love to be so independent. You are my twenty-fourth date. But as long as I can see you, I feel alright."

Jocelyn suggested lightly he could join a group in which he could learn more about self-expression. When she got home, she told him they would not see each other again. He wrote her several letters that all went unanswered.

After a few weeks, Jocelyn found out where he was. Her cousin had started going out with him. If she had asked, Jocelyn would have given her some warning, but she didn't.

Awhile back, Jocelyn had broken up with a fellow who, it turned out, a good friend of hers had an interest in. Jocelyn's friend was kind enough to ask if she would mind if she went out with him. Of course, Jocelyn said she was fine with that and thanked her for being so kind as to ask.

Her friend said, "It just felt right that when a friend wants to go out with someone you just broke up with. It's important they ask you. Jocelyn, you and our friendship are more important to me than a date."

This really warmed Jocelyn's heart. Now if she could only find a date as courteous of her feelings. Still, she'd soldier on. With all the Mr. Wrongs she'd dated, surely Mr. Right was getting closer.

#Click#

Chapter 13

A Singles' Affair

Jocelyn longed for the old married days where Saturday evening was a time for relaxation and sweet togetherness. Could be they would just curl up on the couch with a good book, laptops, or the latest movie in comfy sweats. The two of them snuggled under a shared blanket leaning into each other, holding hands, or four feet reaching for each other in a warm loving tangle.

No great plan or second thought was needed. They just moved around each other as naturally as birds flying in a flock or fish in a school. Movements were fluid, easy, and synchronistic. Touching, always touching.

Since the surprising turn of events leading to their divorce, Jocelyn dreaded Saturdays. There was always pressure to get out and meet new people. The whole single scene was like a long, dark tunnel one had to suffer through to get to the light. And Jocelyn did long for that light. But it seemed so far off.

Well, the big night was rolling around again. Jocelyn and her bestie, Dahlia, were determined to get out there to a singles' event. But often they would call each other at the last minute to concede their true desire to return to comfortable Saturday nights of married past. "How about if we just go to a chick flick tonight?" Sometimes, they'd say it in unison and break out laughing. It was exhausting at their age to get gussied up and go out to some meat market competition.

But, tonight promised to be different. Dahlia had found a large singles' gathering advertised as the pinnacle melding of the most popular online dating sites, dating services, and singles' meetup groups. Everyone that's anyone "out there" would all be "in here."

They agreed to give it a try. After all, it could be no worse than that ghastly New Year's Eve party at the local dance studio. They'd pulled up in front of the dance hall, but neither made a move to get out of the car. They sat in silence as they previewed potential partners for the dance floor as they arrived. There were many pairs of hopeful women (not unlike themselves), about a dozen unaccompanied females, a few couples…and two men.

One of the men seemed to know something no one else did because he was sporting a pair of high-water pants, hemmed above his ankles. The only way to make this worse, which he of course did, was to wear white socks. After the door closed behind him, the two friends looked at each other and burst into uncontrollable laughter until tears flowed. Jocelyn dried her eyes and immediately put the car in gear. They fled the scene as if Mr. Flood-Pants was giving chase.

Once a safe distance away, Jocelyn said with an exasperated tone, "Who knew it could be so difficult to meet an intelligent, centered, confident, kind, financially secure, emotionally stable, and authentically communicative man?"

Dahlia laughed, "Oh, is that all you want?"

She shrugged as she snorted out a laugh. "Well," she managed to blurt out. "I just need ONE!"

They both chuckled and leaned toward each other. Dahlia was the chorus to which Jocelyn sang. They had been close friends for years and were amazingly on the same life path much of the time. Their love and respect for each other was palpable.

It took some doing, but Dahlia managed to persuade Jocelyn that tonight's Single Mingle would be different than that New Year's fiasco. There'd be a great assembly of the most elite, "cream of the crop" single men from all over the city. They both agreed to go without considering any other options for the evening. Dahlia declared, "No backing out!" Jocelyn concurred. Dahlia insisted on driving to further prevent premature escape from this superbly touted event.

Dahlia picked Jocelyn up, plugged the address from the flyer into the GPS, and drove to the event. They landed in front of a decadent, high-class hotel. The meet and greet would be in the extravagantly decorated dining room. As they stood in the doorway, they saw the registration table. The sign said the event fee was forty-five dollars. They froze in place, not unlike deer in headlights, and looked at each other.

Jocelyn was the first to speak. "You know, we each could go to five movies for forty-five dollars and have enough left for popcorn!"

It was Dahlia that kept her resolve. "Remember, no backing out. We're here. We're both having a great hair day, we look fabulous, and we're going in."

Jocelyn realized she was actually holding her breath as they dove in. They paid the fee, and Jocelyn strained to look through the dark entrance to see who was there. Would this be the tunnel that finally led her to the light?

They hesitantly walked into the room. It was buzzing with activity. It looked and sounded like a movie set of *How to Be Single*. There were people mingling around the bar. Platefuls of food were whizzing passed them.

Dahlia and Jocelyn decided to sit at a small table with their drinks to peruse the playing field. They relaxed and caught up with each other. Enjoying themselves, they forgot about all else.

A voice interrupted them in mid laugh. "Would you mind if I join you?" He was a distinguished looking man, nicely dressed, small in stature with a thick, foreign accent. His skin tone had a beautiful olive quality.

Slightly annoyed at the interruption, then, remembering why they were there, "Please do," Jocelyn heard herself say and felt her face force a smile.

After sitting across from Jocelyn, he asked, "Can you guess where I am from?"

The women looked at each other, now remembering they were in the land of flirtatious opening lines and goofy games.

Jocelyn had no idea where he was from and didn't want to guess. The Middle East was experiencing intense turmoil with cultural and religious conflicts mounting. To lighten the situation, she asked in a southern accent, "Darlin', you sound to me like you're from…Texas?"

Dahlia was on board instantly with a version of southern all her own. "Oh no! I know an Oklahoma accent when I hears one!"

All three laughed. "I am from Iran. My name is Hafid, and it is lovely to meet you both."

Just then, a guy wearing the nametag *Steve* appeared. He plopped down near Dahlia and began flirting terribly. "You come here often?" he spitted loudly as he'd clearly already had a few.

She had drunk just enough that he didn't bother her, and she started flirting back just as badly.

In the meantime, Jocelyn learned that Hafid had earned a doctorate in the United States shortly after moving here from Iran. He'd recently authored a book simply because he had things to say. Jocelyn was beginning to be impressed and interested.

The only thing that bothered her was the cultural difference. She'd been married to a man identified with a culture other than her own, and there were some differences that could never be reconciled. She didn't want to experience that great divide again.

Hafid gave Jocelyn his card. "It would please me if you would call so we could get to know each other better."

Jocelyn took the card and placed it in her wallet as if it were valuable currency she didn't want to lose.

Hafid left the table to get everyone more drinks. The progressively more drunken Steve with Dahlia, asked Jocelyn,

"Do you want to be rescued? I can get him to go away."

Jocelyn answered, "No, thank you. I don't really want him to go away."

Dahlia said, "Steve, would you please do that for me?"

After a few minutes of thinking about this, he seemed to finally understand what she meant. Without another word, he got up and left.

The two women were laughing when Hafid approached the table with another drink for each of them.

"Hmm," Dahlia said to Jocelyn. "This man just may be a keeper!"

Hafid pretended not to hear this, but his eyes sparkled as he smiled warmly at Jocelyn.

The evening had been fun and interesting. Both women were glad they'd gone.

A few days later, Jocelyn called Hafid, and they decided to meet for dinner. A few days after that, they took in a movie. They saw each other regularly for several weeks. They were taking a walk along the bay when Jocelyn stopped to take a picture of a flower softly lit by moonlight. When she looked up, she took a picture of Hafid with the backdrop of the orange burst of sunset shimmering on the bay's light-blue surface.

He looked at her and smiled warmly with an expression on his face she'd never seen before.

"What is it?" Jocelyn asked, thinking she might have spinach stuck in her teeth from dinner.

"You. It could be you. You could be the one for me." He said unabashedly.

She was shocked. Flattered, but so taken aback. For as much as she longed to be someone's *one*, she didn't yet know how she felt about him. She said nothing but reached her hand out to him.

Hand in hand, they continued to walk in silence. He was smiling involuntarily. She was trying to regain her balance. This seemed so fast. His pace hastened, he was literally and figuratively moving too fast for her.

Part of her wanted to take the leap and get carried away in the romance of it all. But she feared vertigo from this whirlwind pace.

What was she feeling? She owed him a response to his pronouncement. She looked past him to the bay. The sun had just silently dipped behind the water's horizon, turning the sky into a slow-moving oil painting of bright reds and yellow above the deepening purple water.

"Hafid, I'm loving getting to know you. I do enjoy the time we share. I just need to take this a bit slower. Let's give each other a chance to really know one another."

"I know you," he declared confidently. "I see how you are this caring, beautiful woman. I want only to be with you. You know me. What more is there to know? In my country, we would have already been married. My father was a sheik. He could have taken many wives, but he chose only one. He knew my mother was the only one. I, too, choose to take only one wife, and I now know who that is to be."

She repeated the words in her head. *Sheik…could have taken many wives.* There it was. The great cultural divide. The one trepidation Jocelyn had about this relationship. He was from a different world, with different ideologies about some of the most basic and prevalent cultural values and norms. Could people with such extremely different life paradigms share one life?

Wanting to change the subject before the sun set on their future, Jocelyn said, "I have an idea. I haven't met any of your friends yet. Why don't I join you and your hiking buddies on your hike tomorrow? I love that hiking trail, and it would give me a chance to get to know your friends."

Hafid seemed to stiffen with discomfort. "I don't think that would be possible."

Jocelyn waited for the rest of the sentence providing some explanation, but Hafid offered none. He avoided her gaze by looking out at the now darkening sky. Deep purple clouds were silently moving over blackening water.

"Why would it not be possible?" She looked up at him.

"I walk with three men. We are all doctors," he explained.

She waited, but nothing more came.

"So, is the conversation only of medical topics? That doesn't bother me. I'm simply interested in meeting your friends and going on the hike."

"It's not the topic of conversation that is the problem. You would not understand anything said, no matter the topic. We do not use English when speaking to each other. We are all from Iran and speak in our Persian language of Farsi."

It felt like a thick curtain had dropped between them. They were still hand in hand, yet Jocelyn envisioned a globe of the earth and where each of their respective worlds appeared.

The chasm between them was growing wider.

Jocelyn wanted to explore this further, trying to salvage her hope for their future. "So, when I visit your family in Iran, will everyone be speaking Farsi?"

He stopped walking, took her by the shoulders, and turned her toward him. His eyes smiled gently. "You would be my family here, in America. My Iranian family is not so important to me. I only go there once or twice a year. I would not be able to bring you with me. I cannot bring home an American, blonde-haired, blue-eyed girl that is not a Muslim. But we will be together here, and that is all that matters. No?"

"No." she said sadly. "Family is very important to me. I've been thinking about how to introduce you to my parents. I've imagined the great difficulty with which they would even hear your name. I even considered introducing you as Harry rather than Hafid. I've imagined navigating the conversation to divert attention away from the fact you are Muslim.

"Well," he laughed. "My name, Hafid, means 'the wise one.' Seeing as I am so wise, it would not bother me to be introduced to your family however you see fit. As far as my religious beliefs, they are deep within me, so it is of no consequence as to what anyone else thinks of this."

"So, you do not care that my family would never really know you?" she asked.

"It is only in my heart to know you, be with you. Beyond that, little in the world matters to me."

On one level, this was the most romantic thing anyone had ever said to her, but on another, it was the most disturbing.

Did he want their relationship to be an island for two? Was there to be no community, friends, or family in their lives?

While she longed to have one person, her soul's mate, with whom she could shower her love and share many things, she knew she also desired more to fulfill her soul's longing for a meaningful life. Could this be enough?

When they said good night that evening, Jocelyn had a feeling it would be the last time they saw each other. While she did love being with him, she knew he wanted to move forward and be married. It was futile to continue in a relationship that did not ultimately fulfill both their needs.

Jocelyn knew herself well enough to know important aspects of her life included extended family, friends, spiritual community, and she wanted an ever-expanding role in giving back to society. She wanted someone who could walk that path with her. The life she wanted was large and full.

As much as she was attracted to Hafid and what he had to offer, she knew she didn't want to live on a deserted island with only him. She'd have to let him go to make room for a man who shared her life vision.

Jocelyn realized that although she was no closer to finding a man with whom she could share a loving life, it did enhance her own self-knowledge. This was a great step in her ability to navigate this process with clarity and self-respect. She was beginning to understand what she wanted and what she didn't want. Even if she didn't succeed in falling in love with this man, she was actually beginning to fall in love. With herself.

#Click#

Chapter 14

BOB'S BIG BOY

After finding each other on the Still in Our Prime dating site, Jocelyn and Bob made plans to meet in their first phone call. He suggested they meet at Don's restaurant right across from the movie theater in mall. They'd have dinner then go to a movie.

Parking was always a challenge, so Jocelyn arrived a few minutes early and found her way to the theater. She looked all around, and there were no restaurants named Don's in sight.

She asked a well-dressed woman waiting to buy theater tickets if she knew where it was, and the woman answered, "There's no Don's in this mall, but if you want equally dreadful cuisine, there's a Rudy's." She pointed about fifty feet away to a red-and-white checkered diner-looking place with a large flashing sign that said Rudy's.

As Jocelyn entered, she passed a twenty-foot plastic statue of a waitress with a skirt that was about six inches long. As she looked up, three feet of shiny red plastic panties reflected the light back to her. She kept walking, trying not to just turn around and leave.

Her date was nowhere to be found so she got a table and sat down. She texted, letting him know where she was seated.

He texted back, "OMG. Took nap (sleeping man emoji) and overslept (clock emoji). Will be there in thirty."

She ordered an iced tea, wondering why she was waiting.

Bob finally arrived, slowly sauntering in. He stopped for a moment to admire the red panties. A long moment.

Seriously? She considered hiding behind the huge menu and ducking out after he passed her.

After studying the menu for the forty-five minutes it took Bob to arrive, she had decided to order the fish dinner. The only other things available were greasy hamburgers and salads. Salads at hamburger joints generally were not appealing.

Bob picked up the menu. "Hi there. When I come here, I always share a salad."

Just then, the waitress came over. Bob said quickly, "We'll be sharing the Mediterranean salad."

"Do you want a basket of bread with that?" the waitress said through popping gum.

"I don't eat bread," he told the waitress, "Just bring crackers. LOTS of crackers." He ordered water with lemon, for two.

"Did you want some sugar for your lemonade?" The waitress laughed.

He nodded yes. And both he and the waitress laughed!

Jocelyn was beginning to feel like a third wheel on this

date. When the waitress started to walk away, Jocelyn called her back. "I'll have another iced tea, please." That added another $2.00 to the total tab of $6.50.

Bob had reported on his online profile he was fit and trim. Well, that might have been true back in the day, but this man perhaps hadn't looked in a mirror in a few years.

For the first time, he made eye contact with Jocelyn. "The woman I'm looking for can't be fluffy."

"Fluffy?"

"I have Jet Skis, and she to be able to pull herself out of the water to get back on when we fall."

He was *fluffy*, but she didn't remind him of this fact.

"Women our age just don't take good care of themselves." He stuffed another two whole crackers in his mouth. "I used to be a millionaire, but after the divorce I have to eat crackers and water."

She thought, *why do I always meet millionaires after they lose it all?*

He continued, "Well, after the divorce, I just wanted to get married. So, I married another woman, also named Debbie. Big mistake. So, if you and I get married, we must sign those papers to protect my estate. And yours, too, of course."

There was a piece of lettuce clinging to the side of his mouth. She couldn't take a moment more and tried to interrupt, but cracker crumbs were flying in her direction with no relief in sight. He kept talking.

"I want to tell you something," he said. "I talk to God. And the good Lord talks back. I know things that most people don't know. When you and I become a couple, you will have a very good life. Of course, we'll go to church every Sunday and follow whatever God tells us to do. I've always heard him but didn't listen, but I've changed. I'm a lot happier now. The only thing missing is you."

She took a deep breath. "Bob, I'm going to be brutally honest here. I think your number one focus is God. While I respect that and have very strong spiritual values, I don't think we share the same path in that regard. I also suspect you are politically conservative. Is that right?"

"That's not a problem for me. If you don't want me voting Republican, I just won't vote."

"The fact you are willing to forego your vote is actually worse than your political affiliation differing from mine."

Bob looked at his watch as if he hadn't heard a word she said. "If we are going to make this movie, we better get going. Especially because I forgot the tickets in the car."

She spoke loudly so he heard her. "What I'm trying to tell you is that I'm not going to the movie, but you should go now so you can catch the beginning." She probably should have had more than one phone conversation with Bob before making the date. Perhaps asked better questions to discern if they had enough in common before setting up a meeting.

While walking to her car, she noticed her favorite store in the mall was having a sale. Rather than have the day be a total loss, she went shopping and had a lovely afternoon.

#Click#

Chapter 15

EXPECTATIONS OR ANXIETY?

Jocelyn had tried a few free or inexpensive online dating sites to get the lay of the land. Sites like PlentyofLosers. com, YourLastChance.com, and CatchYourMatch.com (a single's catch and release program). The men she met through these sites were either "retired" (an oft used code word for unemployed), "helping his mother" (code for doesn't have a place of his own), "newly single" (the last in a series of failed marriages just ended), "easy-going" (he has nothing left to lose), or otherwise undesirable. Jocelyn decided to up her game.

She joined a dating service, called Great Expectations. They created a video of each member, capturing a few moments describing—in their own words and in their own way—what they sought in a soul mate. These were then uploaded to the member's site.

The short clips provided Jocelyn a sneak preview of potential matches. Unlike the still profile pictures, some of which were older than her twelve-year-old dog or altered with Photoshop, members had to show up and record the video on site. The videos showed how each member expressed him or herself. One could see how the pressure of three minutes of television fame was handled. Jocelyn viewed these three-minute trailers to see if her interest would be piqued enough to want to view the full-length movie or meet the star.

The cost of this service was far more than most online dating sites, but it provided a close up and personal look at the actual person. Jocelyn was set up with an interview with a personal matchmaker. The woman had a perpetual smile that seemed glued to her face and, in Jocelyn's perception, was overly enthusiastic.

"I'm so glad you came in!" Sheila exclaimed a bit too loudly. "You're just the kind of person our male clients are seeking! Your age group really needs more women who are youthful, active, attractive, and are serious about finding someone. You'll do great in this program."

Bet you say that to all the girls, Jocelyn wanted to say but kept the comment to herself.

After taking care of the paperwork for joining the program, Sheila led her into a small room with a backdrop, an HD camera perched atop a tripod, mounted lights, and cables snaking their way around the floor. She instructed Jocelyn to carefully walk through the reptilian-like wires without tripping and take a seat on the stool to which all the equipment pointed. Jocelyn nodded, smiled weakly, and began to sweat profusely as she carefully entered what felt like her own personal interrogation room.

She had thought she would easily ad-lib her video. She'd been a teacher, so speaking off the cuff for three minutes generally wasn't a problem. But as she sat in that tight space with all the equipment and walls closing in on her, she realized she was at a loss. Without knowing to whom she was even talking, how would she know the right things to say? How does one boil down a lifetime of experience, love, pain, and healing into three minutes? She had one-hundred-and-eighty-seconds to present a life articulated in a manner that would attract a life partner. She wished she had prepared.

Sam, the camera guy, came lumbering into the room in a huff. "Sorry for the wait, running late. That last woman wanted to tell her whole sad life story, and she broke down crying in the middle. We had to wait until the swelling in her eyes went down. Now, I'm running twenty minutes late. Okay, you ready?"

Without waiting for a response, he hit the record button and a red light popped on, like the starting pistol at an Olympic race urging her to begin.

"Sam," Jocelyn said softly, "Could you please turn that off and give me a moment to consider what I'd like to say?"

Sam looked visibly annoyed as he hit the button again, turning off the pressure cooker. "Just say your name, where you are from, and what you're looking for."

What was she looking for? How did she talk about why she was there without upsetting Sam by bursting into tears? Should she say, "My life is wonderful! The only way it could be better is if I had someone with whom to share it!" Had her life really become such a cliché?

Sam began to pace in the two feet behind the camera, getting his ankles tangled in cables. He looked at her pleadingly. She nodded at him to appease him. He again pushed the dreaded button.

"Hi. My name's Jocelyn. I never dreamt I would be doing this." *Be positive!* "But this seems like a fun way to meet new people, a new person." *Yikes!* "There are lots of things I love to do. Dancing, biking, boating, movies, theater. I even enjoy food shopping if shared with someone special. Care to dance?"

After an excruciating three minutes that seemed more like an interminable six hours, the red light finally went off. She had no idea what she'd said, only that it was over. She walked briskly to her car, shedding a few layers of sweaty clothes on the way.

She'd considered requesting a do-over, but within two days she had requests for a date by a few Great Expectations, or High Anxiety men.

The first, Han, was a man whose profile seemed to reflect values shared by Jocelyn. He'd recently lost his wife after a long illness and presented himself as a man earnestly seeking a marriage partner. He was employed in a high-tech position and lived in a town about twenty-five minutes from her.

Upon their first few meetings, Jocelyn realized Han was a sweet, kind, and quiet man. Their conversations flowed easily, and several day trips proved to be quite pleasurable for both. He was intelligent and thoughtful, and she found her affection for him growing.

Han told Jocelyn he'd like to make her a special dinner at his home. She accepted his invitation, looking forward to spending time with him in his own home.

Upon first entering his house, there was a large shelf over the fireplace that featured a framed picture of a pretty, middle-aged Asian-American woman. Next to the photo was a vase with a freshly cut, bright-red rose. "That's my wife," Han said quietly. "She died a year and a half ago. I cut a fresh flower from her garden for her every day. Can I show you the rest of the house?" he asked her.

She nodded, and he took the lead. They entered a large bedroom, furnished tastefully. A silver purse with a gold clasp sat atop the large dresser, wide open like an invitation. "That's my wife's pocketbook," he said when he noticed her looking at it. "I've not moved it since the night I took her to the hospital."

Jocelyn respectfully looked away. Perhaps she had misunderstood. She thought he'd said it had been over a year and a half since his wife's death.

The walk-in closet door was wide open, and Jocelyn couldn't help but peek in. She found that exactly one half of the closet was occupied by darkly colored suits, a variety of ties, and crisp, white shirts. They hung neatly and obediently, the way school children line up when instructed by their teacher.

The other side of the closet was also full. A woman's complete wardrobe hung organized by skirts, dresses, slacks, and gowns. Many were further contained in plastic bags, appearing to have been recently dry cleaned.

On each side of the closet, shoes lined up on the floor, each pair seeming to accessorize a pair of tuxedo pants or a ball gown. They faced off with a pair from the other side as if they were formally dressed couples on the dance floor ready for the next waltz, just waiting for the music to begin again.

"I can't bring myself to remove any of her things," he said with eyes down. "Even after a year and a half, I just couldn't bear to do it."

"It's okay, Han. When you're ready, you'll know what to do." Jocelyn said kindly, all the while thinking that until he let go of his wife, there was literally and figuratively no room for another woman in his house or his life.

After this visit to his home, Jocelyn realized he wasn't ready to move on. Han was a wonderful man, one she could love. But she would give him the space and time he needed to deal with his ghost, the one he wished would never go away.

As for Jocelyn, she was trying to discern her own readiness to move forward. It was interesting, she thought as she drove home. We all have baggage from our past. She'd just never seen it unpacked and organized quite so neatly before. She considered what ghosts in her own past got in the way of saying yes to a new possibility. She realized her fear of being hurt again was taking up way too much space in her life. She would work on evicting her own ghosts to make room for new possibilities. Hopefully, Han would do the same. Who knows? When the time was right and they were both ready, the music would begin and the dance could start anew.

#Click#

Chapter 16

SPEEDY SENIORS

Jocelyn decided to date the way she did everything else—all in. The holidays were rolling around again, culminating in New Year's Eve. Her assignment was to find a kissable date by the stroke of midnight. She was determined not to be caught standing by herself while everyone else in the world, in consecutive time zones, was smooching in the New Year.

She decided to try speed dating, thinking this might move things along in expedited fashion. She signed up for the fifty plus Speedy Seniors gathering the following Saturday night.

Jocelyn arrived early and was directed to the bar. She rarely frequented bars, especially on her own. She was considering waiting in her car for a few minutes or forgoing the whole nerve-wracking experience and going to the movies. She noticed another woman in the room looking around nervously.

She approached her. "Hi, I'm Jocelyn. Are you here for speed dating?"

"Oh, hi. I'm Betty. Yes, I am." She looked around to see if anyone could hear. "But I'm seriously considering bolting. Want to go to a movie?"

Jocelyn laughed, since that was exactly what she'd been thinking. When she drove in, she'd noticed there was a movie theater just across the street with a movie she wanted to see.

"I really truly do, but I'm also curious to check this speed dating thing out. I mean, what's the worst that could happen?"

"A really bad date…over and over and over, eight times in one night!" Betty started heading for the door.

"Perhaps we should have a drink." Jocelyn suggested, surprising herself because she didn't drink on dates.

By then, others had arrived. Just as the bartender offered the two women their drinks, a man approached and handed the bartender a twenty-dollar bill. "Let me get that. Hello ladies, my name is Curt. I've done this gig several times. I'm sure you'll have fun. Now that you are here, I'm sure I'll enjoy myself too."

Betty and Jocelyn looked at each other. They tried to hold back their laughter. Betty cocked the top of her head towards the door a few times with her eyebrows held high, as a secret invitation. That was more than Jocelyn could stand, and she burst out laughing. Betty joined in, and Curt laughed without a clue as to what was so funny.

Another man walked over and introduced himself. "I'm William. You ladies must be first timers tonight."

Jocelyn and Betty said they were. They made small talk with William cracking a few corny jokes, but he was nice and sincerely trying to put them at ease.

Just then, everyone was called into the event room.

As they followed the group, Betty leaned into Jocelyn to whisper, "Last chance to bail, girlfriend."

Jocelyn whispered back, "If you find the man of your dreams here tonight, you can thank me later." She took Betty by the arm and pulled her along into the potential "chamber of horrors."

The room was set up with tables, each with two chairs facing each other. Every woman sat at her own assigned dating station. The men were to move around the room much like musical chairs on steroids. Each "date" was allotted eight minutes with the end signified by a loud *ding* of the bell.

Jocelyn made herself comfortable at her assigned table. Betty waved while rolling her eyes from her spot across the room. Jocelyn reviewed the paper in front of her. There were squares on the page, numbered one through eight, and a place for notes next to each one. At the bottom of each were two words from which to choose: YES or NO.

DING! Jocelyn looked up, and there was already a man sitting across from her with a strange expression, twitching nervously. His dark-rimmed glasses seem to jump with each tic. She waited for him to say something while he did the same.

"Okay... my name is Jocelyn. My friends call me Jocelyn. Do you have a name other than number six?"

"Yes. Norman."

Silence.

"So, you come here often, Norman?" Jocelyn teased.

"No. I've never done this before. I'm basically a workaholic and don't date. My coworker, Mitch, suggested I try this and bought me a ticket to come. I didn't really want to."

Jocelyn peeked at her watch. One minute had nearly elapsed. Now she understood what Betty meant.

"What do you do, Norman?"

"I do data entry for a large corporation downtown."

"That sounds interesting," she lied.

Silence.

Two minutes down, six to go.

More silence.

"So, what are you looking for?" she asked him.

"What do you mean?"

"Are you looking for a date? A friend? A serious relationship? What?"

"I don't really think I am looking for anything. Just wanted Mitch to stop bugging me about going to one of these."

"Okay then," Jocelyn sighed. "I'm so sorry, but will you excuse me? Just need to run to the restroom for a moment." Or five minutes and thirty seconds.

As she walked to the restroom, she caught Betty's attention. Betty was smiling and flashed Jocelyn an excited thumbs up. Jocelyn put one thumb up with as much enthusiasm as she could muster.

She washed her hands and checked her watch. *Hmm, I seem to still have another two minutes in Norman-land.* She dried her hands. Very slowly.

When she returned to the table, Norman was still sitting there. Just as she sat down, the blessed bell rang out with a *DING!*

"It was great meeting you, Norman." She smiled, trying to sound sincere.

At least she had finally found a solution to the problem of time passing by way too quickly. If she ever wanted time to stand still, she'd call Norman. She looked on her form and circled NO.

The next man approached at a trot from his last station. As he sat down, he reached for Jocelyn's hand. "Hi, Number Two, I'm Number Eight, but I'm hoping we are each other's number one. My name's Neil. And yours?"

"Hi, Neil. I'm Jocelyn. Nice to meet you."

"Jocelyn, that's a nice name. Unusual."

"Thank you. It's short for Jocelyn. So, Neil, what do you do when you're not charming speed daters?"

"I'm a video photographer. I'm excited by my work as I recently had a client who needed aerial shots. I have a degree in engineering arts, so I built a drone with a high-definition camera attached. The client was thrilled about not having the expense of renting a helicopter. Want to see how it works?"

"Sure," Jocelyn said sincerely, since this man was willing do to some of the heavy lifting in this date.

Neil pulled out his phone and clicked on a video. It was a beautiful shot of the ocean from high above exactly as the sun set. This actually interested her as she was shooting a video series of her own.

Impressed with the fluid motion of the video panning the beach. "That's amazing. I just needed a very similar shot. I bought a ticket for a balloon ride up in Del Mar to get that shot. It was expensive but did the trick. Do you have control of the drone's movement while also controlling the zoom lens?"

As he pulled up an image of the drone with the camera attached… *DING!*

"What? That fast?" Jocelyn felt like she was in anti-Norman-land where time was sped up. "Do you have a card so I might hire your flying robot for future video shoots?"

"Oh, if you want my drone, you'll have to want me," Neil answered coyly. "Just circle the YES for number eight, and we can continue our conversation later."

She did just that.

When she looked up, number five was sitting down at her table. He was a very handsome, well-dressed man with salt-and-pepper hair, blue eyes, and a stethoscope around his neck.

"Did you call for a medic?" he asked.

"Not that I know of, but the night's still young. Maybe you should stick around in case I feel overly excited in the next eight minutes."

"I hope you do."

"I'm Jocelyn. What do they call you? Doc?"

"I'm Joe. I'm actually a paramedic. But you can call me whatever you wish. Just as long as you call me." He paused. "I'm sorry. That was really desperate sounding, wasn't it? It is nerve wracking having just eight minutes to make a first impression. Can we start again?" He pulled his hands off the table and yelled, "CLEAR!"

Jocelyn laughed. "You're funny, Joe. Why haven't I seen you online or at any other events? Where have you been all my life?"

"I've been married most of my life. Until my wife lost hers, that is. We celebrated our thirtieth anniversary, next thing you know, she has a heart attack. I save people every day. Restarting hearts is my specialty. Ironically, I couldn't help her. That's something I have to live with."

"Joe, I'm certain you know it's not your fault. There all kinds of different reasons for a heart to stop. Some of those reasons can't be overcome with CPR or defibrillation."

"So where did you get YOUR medical degree from, Dr. Jocelyn?"

"Why, my proud alma mater is the infamous University of *Grey's Anatomy*."

They both laughed as the bell went off. They simultaneously circled YES.

Next up to bat was a familiar face from the bar. "Hi there! I'm Curt."

"Oh, yes. Thanks for the drink earlier."

"You're welcome, darlin'. I love making the newbies feel comfortable. I can spot them a mile away. Look like frightened rabbits, poor things. A drink usually calms them down. Or at least makes them more interesting to visit."

Jocelyn was curious. "So exactly how many times have you done speed dating?"

He leaned in. "Too many to count."

"You're single and still looking?"

Curt laughed. "The looking is the fun part. I've been married before, honey, so while I love looking, I'm not really interested in finding anything more than a really good time. I'm guessing you're a really good time. Am I right?"

Jocelyn glanced at the clock behind Curt's head. Five and a half more minutes.

"I'm so sorry, but I think I need to relieve myself of the drink you bought me." *And of your company.* She got up and went to the ladies' room. As she walked across the room, she checked out how Betty was doing, to find her in the midst of a huge yawn. When she looked to see who was sitting across from Betty, there was—Norman.

Betty managed to break free to follow her new BFF to the restroom. She walked slowly and quietly into the ladies' room while Norman sat motionless at her table. The minute Jocelyn and Betty saw each other, they both released the laughter that was dying to come out. Tears streaked their cheeks as they laughed, sobbed, and guffawed uncontrollably. Betty snorted repeatedly, and Jocelyn got the hiccups. There was a woman in a stall who started laughing until she cried. She came out of the stall and nearly fell on the floor. They were all leaning on and hugging each other while the hysterics continued.

"Kill me now." Betty begged.

"You?" the woman from the stall cried out. "Have you met Norman yet?" That started all of them laughing uncontrollably again.

Jocelyn checked her watch. "Hey, we only have thirty seconds to get back to our speed dating cockpits. No pun intended!"

All three women checked the mirror as they were leaving. The tears had carried half their makeup down to their chins. None of them seemed to care.

They got back just in time for Betty to bid adieu to Norman and for Jocelyn to send Curt on his way.

William from earlier was next. He wasn't the kind of man she was physically attracted to, but he was kind if a bit overeager, and the time went by quickly.

The next few dates that came to Jocelyn were uneventful, and she began to mix them all up in her head. She couldn't remember which one was an electrician and which was the accountant. It didn't much matter to her. Not until her very last date, Sean.

Sean was the first man whose smile made it all the way to his eyes. His face was handsome, but even more importantly, it was warm. His eyes were a deep turquoise color and seemed to have a wisdom sparkling from them.

"Is this seat taken?" he asked.

"It's been waiting for you." She was surprised by her own boldness.

"Yes. I've been waiting for you, as well." Sean responded easily. "Are you having fun, tonight?"

"It's *interesting.*"

Sean laughed. "Is that code for 'I'd never want to do this again?'"

She admittedly nodded her head. "Not sure what I expected, but it's just not as easy as I thought it would be. Why is it so difficult to meet an intelligent, kind person who is able to engage in real communication?"

"I know what you mean," Sean agreed. "I didn't expect to find Ms. Right tonight, but it would be lovely to find someone with whom eight minutes doesn't feel like a life sentence."

They both laughed. Jocelyn realized, for the first time tonight, she was actually enjoying herself.

"So, Ms. Jocelyn, what do you enjoy doing when you're not dating eight men at a time?"

"Oh, this is unusual for me, I usually date nine. Just kidding. I love playing tourist in San Diego. Some of my favorite pastimes are walks on the beach, swimming, biking, dancing, drives to the mountains. I particularly enjoy watching the hang gliders leaping off the cliff and soaring over the ocean. You?"

"I second the motion on the watching others running off the cliffs. I've thought of trying it, but I am rather attached to terra firma.

"Yes, for me the less firma, the more terror!"

Just when she thought she'd really like to ask him more about himself—the bell announced the end of the evening.

As Sean stood he said, "Jocelyn, I hope I'll have the chance to see you again."

"I'd like that as well. It's been a real pleasure meeting you, Sean." And she felt happy that she actually meant it.

Jocelyn found having eight dates in the span of a few hours exhausting, and by the end of the event, she couldn't keep the line-up of men straight. She couldn't read the notes she had written as she had tried to maintain eye contact while writing and the result was a scribbled mess. Besides, sometimes the allotted time was just too short to get a real sense of a person. Of course, at other times, the remaining seven minutes were painfully long and difficult to endure.

However, there was one very beneficial perk to the speed dating practice. Even though she met eight men, she only needed to prepare once. One shower, one outfit, one trip, one evening.

When the organizer called her the next day, he said that she was the big winner with four mutual matches. She would think about if this introduction was just a bit too fast, or speedy, to qualify these fellows for a potential date.

While this had been an interesting experience (maybe that *was* code for never wanting to do it again) part of her had wished she and Betty had gone to that movie.

#Click#

Chapter 17

Moonless Night

During the speed-dating event, Jocelyn had selected four men with whom she might be willing to meet on a date. Each of them had also selected her. Feeling a bit shy about this process, she decided to go out with William first. She wasn't attracted to him physically, but his kindness had impressed her. What could it hurt to share a meal? He might end up being interesting. Who knows? Maybe this Poindexter could turn into a Ken doll if she got to know him better.

On the phone he said, "I'm thrilled to take you to my absolute favorite restaurant on La Jolla Shores. It's a trendy spot as it's the sole restaurant on this legendary stretch of beach. It's romantic and celebrated as having the best food in the area. We're lucky to get the reservation."

"That sounds wonderful. Thank you for making such a nice plan."

"What time shall I pick you up?" William asked.

Remembering Barb's admonishment about having an escape vehicle on the first few dates she responded, "I'll meet you there. I know right where it is."

"Why would we take two cars? Parking may be difficult to find. I don't mind picking you up at all. What's your address?" William persisted.

"I have an appointment prior to our date," she lied. "It would be easier if I come directly from there. I just looked it up, and they have valet parking so no problem. See you then."

After they hung up, she wondered if that rule about never getting in the car with a man on the first several dates was too stringent. After all, they'd already met. He seemed harmless. Well, it was done now, so she'd keep the plan as it was.

On Friday evening as she prepared for the date, she tried recalling what William looked like. It was always embarrassing to walk into a restaurant finding several men waiting and not recognizing which was waiting for her. She recalled he'd been on the corpulent side, with that teddy bear look. While it's not what most women seek, hugs could be soft and cozy. Not like that health nut she'd dated who felt like a bicycle when you hugged him.

William was a bit taller, probably six feet. Since she was a mere five feet two inches, every inch beyond five foot ten had her staring at a navel. Since they sat at a table on their eight-minute speed date, she hadn't really noticed his height until he talked to her after the event. He was a bit of a loud talker. She liked calm and quiet, but she attributed his volume to a noisy environment. She was almost talking herself out of going but reminded herself it was just dinner and not a wedding. Besides, she was having a great hair day.

The phone rang, and it was Dahlia. "Hey gal pal!"

"How's the prepping going? Hair and makeup behaving, or do you need minor surgery before leaving?"

"Very funny. I'm meeting William, so I think I'm good."

"Oh." Dahlia sounded disappointed. "You're going out with the safe one instead of the hot doctor?"

"He's a paramedic. Yes, I guess I'm practicing for one that I really care about."

"Still scared? I wish you'd see yourself as I see you. Nothing to worry about. He and his stethoscope would be lucky to spend time around that heart of yours. I better let you go for your 'rehearsal date' with William. I'll expect a full report."

After they hung up, Jocelyn considered Dahlia's words. She was right. All Jocelyn wanted was a life partner who shared the same values, interests, and consciousness. Yet she picked safe, unattractive guys because she didn't believe she could succeed with any man she'd actually want by her side.

She remembered something she'd read from her favorite poet, Rumi. "Your task is not to seek for love, but merely to seek and find all the barriers within yourself that you have built against it."

She wrote it down to consider after her practice date. But now it was time to go.

When she arrived, her jaw dropped at the elegance of the dining room. The settings on the tables were already a feast for the eyes. Her attention was split between the aromatic smells of gourmet food and the fact the entire back wall was a window unveiling a panorama of the Pacific Ocean. The scene changed minute to minute as the sky reddened with the sunset. The beach was just steps from the tables. The windows kept only the ocean air from blowing her blonde hair.

She remembered why she was there and noticed William sitting in the lobby with a single rose. "Madame." He presented her with the gift with a deep bow. "Your table awaits."

The hostess led them to a window side table, which he had obviously arranged. It was a table with an exquisite view.

"It's an impeccable night." William pointed to the window with Vanna White flare. "It will be a moonless night. We can enjoy the stars unadulterated by that pesky moon illuminating the beach and ruining the view."

Jocelyn preferred a full moon with the light shimmering off the water. She would marvel at the shadows the moon threw, mirroring the palm trees and even her own body. But she said nothing. If William liked a dark ocean setting, so be it.

They had a lovely meal and talked for three hours. He insisted she try some of the most expensive dishes. They were, indeed, delectable. She was impressed with William's generosity.

"I've heard about this place," Jocelyn began. "I'm glad to have had a chance to try it. You were right; it's very special."

"Well, I've been doing really well in the stock market these days. This president is great for helping the rich get richer."

She thought, *that's true. He also helps the poor get poorer.* In these days of political *them* and *us*, she knew it was never a good idea to argue politics over dinner. William was a good conversationalist. She appreciated his articulateness, if not his opinions.

She realized she was not attracted to him. If he asked her out again, she'd tell him no in the kindest way possible.

When they left the restaurant, instead of going toward the cars, William took her arm and led her in the direction of the beach. "It's time for the best part of the evening!" he announced enthusiastically. "Time to walk down to the water's edge and enjoy the stars of a moonless night."

Suddenly, Jocelyn heard Barb's voice in her head as she advised staying near other people on a first date. Like a four-alarm warning, she recalled the urgency with which Barb had cautioned.

Jocelyn looked up at William. "I'd prefer we walk on the lighted sidewalk rather than go all the way down to the water's edge," she gently told him.

"Come on. When do you ever get to see stars in San Diego? This is such a rare opportunity. We've just spent three hours together. Do I really seem like a danger to you?"

Jocelyn reconsidered. He'd been charming while they ate. He'd treated her to an unusually opulent meal and had been nothing but nice. It actually was atypical to see so many stars. They would be more visible away from the restaurant lights. She hesitantly agreed.

They left their shoes near the restaurant and made their way through the sand, about three hundred feet, sliding through the sandy hill to the water's edge. As they walked through the deep sand, he reached for her hand. Hand in hand, they arrived at the water.

He pulled her close to him and gave her a deep kiss. She began to back up. His hand gripped hers more tightly. His other hand wrapped around her back.

He said in a voice gruffer than the one he'd used at dinner, "Hey, where do you think you're going?"

"I thought we could take a walk." She tried not to sound nervous.

"How about we stay right here, and you think of a way to say thank you for that hundred-and-fifty-dollar dinner you just ate?" He pulled her close again with the vice grip he had on her right hand. Then, he slid his right arm under her jacket, around her back and quickly pushed his hand down the back of her pants. He grabbed at her flesh while his hungry mouth was searching for hers.

It took her a moment to realize what was happening. She looked toward the restaurant but knew any screams would be drowned out by the ocean waves crashing at their feet. The moonless night guaranteed no one would see her unless she could make it back to the lighted area near the restaurant.

She had to act fast. She dropped into a deep knee bend to extricate his hand from her pants.

He was surprised by this sudden move, but he still had a firm hold on her right hand. He raised their clasped hands between them as he laughed at her.

She stood and in one quick movement, turned her arm, placing all her weight toward his thumb. She had learned this maneuver in a self-defense class but had never tried it. His thumb could not hold her. She stood and was free.

She immediately ran as fast as the deep sand would allow. It felt like she was moving in slow motion. Without looking back, she continued clawing through what felt like a mountain of quicksand. Her heart pounded in her chest. Her quickened pulse rang so loudly in her ears she could no longer hear the ocean. When she finally reached the lighted sidewalk in front of the restaurant and was in the safe company of strangers, she turned to see if he was chasing her. He was nowhere in sight.

As she took deep breaths to recover from her escape, she found and put on her shoes. She picked up William's shoes and thought she'd toss them in the garbage. They were Italian leather and looked brand new. They must have cost hundreds of dollars. She noticed a homeless man sitting on the sidewalk.

"Excuse me," she said to him. "Could you use these?" She handed them to him to inspect.

"They're my size. Are you sure?" he asked.

She nodded while looking around for William.

He said, "Thanks. Call me lucky."

Jocelyn smiled at him. They both got lucky tonight.

She asked a couple walking toward the parking lot if they wouldn't mind walking her to her car, which they did. She drove home, zigzagging down a variety of streets, in case William was following her.

"So," she said aloud to herself once safely home. "Rules about not getting in a man's car or being alone with someone you don't know in an isolated place are definitely smart rules to follow. From now on, no exceptions."

She laughed at herself thinking that William had seemed like the "safe" choice. From now on, she would start tearing down those barriers and go for what she really wanted.

Later, she called the speed dating organizers and the police to report William. Jocelyn hoped to prevent him from ever assaulting another woman. While she had finally tried speed dating, the only thing she got from it was a man who moved way too fast.

#Click#

Chapter 18

WHERE THE BOYS ARE

Jocelyn and Dahlia were having lunch and reminiscing about all the ways they had tried to meet men.

"Remember when you took up golf?" Dahlia laughed.

"Don't laugh at me," Jocelyn said. "At least I had the gumption to try. It's a very humbling game."

"You joined that threesome of women and played every Saturday morning. Did you get any better?" Dahlia teased.

"Well, I have a confession. After they realized I wasn't keeping score, they kicked me out of the game."

"You got fired from golf?"

"The goal wasn't to become a pro, if you recall."

"Right, did you meet any men?"

"No."

"Really? On Saturdays, the golf course must have been crawling with men."

"Yes, there were a lot of men there, but they were very focused…on their own balls."

Dahlia gasped.

"Not those, their golf balls."

"Jocelyn, you're a total jock. When you retired from golf, or rather got fired, you took up racquet ball. You even joined that sweaty gym, the one where all the hunks hung out. Did you end up with a hunk? You had your eye on that cute Black guy with all the muscles. What happened?"

"I ended up with a black…eye. I tried hitting the ball off the back wall like I saw others doing and, unlike the men there, it came right at me. After the embarrassing visit to the ER, I never played again."

"Remember that time we went to the law library?" Dahlia giggled.

"We sat there for two hours with no eye contact from anyone but each other. Then, we put on glasses to look more studious."

"Yeah, that's about when you had the brilliant idea to go sit near the men's bathroom."

"I needed to use the facilities. I figured eventually we'd see everyone who was there for more than an hour."

"Yeah, but that didn't work because they were in too much of a hurry going in, and too busy straightening their clothes when they came out."

"Remember the time we went bowling on league night. That was a fiasco."

"I couldn't help it. The ball was too heavy, and I tore a tendon in my shoulder. At least the ER had tons of cute docs running around."

"Yes, but all those emergent patients kept bleeding profusely, so we weren't even noticed."

"So sorry I wasn't bleeding enough for you!" Jocelyn rolled her eyes.

"Then," Dahlia added. "We read that article about NOT looking. The theory was if you stopped looking, that's when he shows up and love just happens. It was a nice break, and I have to admit I loved binge watching *Grey's Anatomy* and *Chicago Fire.*"

"I guess you're supposed to get off your couch while you're not looking." They both laughed.

"It's definitely not from a lack of trying," said Jocelyn.

"How many dates do you think we each went on?"

"I don't know, but if dating were a full-time job, I'd be due a two-week paid vacation."

Dalia went on. "Bad breath, BO, sex addicts, cat hair guy, quiet man, loud talker, stalker dude, texting guy, sure thang guy, indecisive man, dog breath, and women watcher."

"I'm getting despondent. Want to go to a movie?"

They started laughing.

#Click#

Chapter 19

WATERCOOLER WALTZING

The sunlit, sapphire sky hovered above the street fair like a protective dome. It was a uniquely San Diego day in which the warmth of the sun gently kissed your face while cool breezes caressed you like a silk scarf. This was the kind of day that commanded extreme joy, even on a first date.

As they headed down the art fair's booth-lined street, Doug took Jocelyn's hand with a comfort and confidence as if he had done it every day of their lives. At first, it surprised her, but she allowed herself to relax and just revel in the ease of it.

The street, closed to cars, provided a sheltered oasis reminiscent of a more peaceful and carefree time. A lively fusion of folk, classical, and Celtic music wafted from multiple stages. That, combined with the smells of strong coffee, freshly cut flowers, newly baked cakes intermingling with steaming grilled onions and peppers, left Jocelyn light headed and happy.

Doug brought her into a booth selling water containers on hand-carved wooden stands. The ceramic containers were all hand painted with distinctly unique leaves and flowers. She thought of buying the one with the green grapevines as it conjured up an image of Tuscany.

Suddenly, she became aware of her favorite song permeating her senses from a nearby stage. Her body involuntarily swayed ever so slightly with the beat. Doug, seeming to read her body and mind, lifted her hand and twirled her into a turn. When she'd spun clear around, Jocelyn stood before him and their smiling eyes met. He put his other arm around her waist and off they went into a waltz right in the middle of that water container tent. The shoppers in the tent and those walking by stopped to watch.

Jocelyn felt her face expanding into a smile larger than she'd worn in a long time. This felt like Disneyland for adults, an exciting E-ticket ride, the one for which she'd waited in line for years. The world spun into a blur, only Doug's face remained in focus. The sound of applause interrupted her reverie and let her know the music had stopped.

The salesman asked, "So how long have you folks been married, and what's your secret?"

Jocelyn blushed as she realized the small crowd was motionless, waiting for an answer. "Oh no, we're not married. This is actually our first date."

A woman in a brightly colored sun hat with a price tag swinging from the brim, likely purchased at the neighboring booth said, "Wow, you look like you've been together for years. How did you happen to meet?"

Jocelyn looked at Doug, and he chimed in. "We met through an online dating site, called LookingForLove.com.

But from now on, I'll call it LookNoFurther.com." And then he gave Jocelyn their first kiss, the first of many.

Jocelyn and Doug dated for several weeks, each encounter taking them deeper into each other's lives. It was a huge moment when Doug invited Jocelyn to his home for dinner to meet his three children.

"I'd love that." she responded quickly.

The following Friday evening, when she pulled up to his house, her nervousness was palpable. She never had children. She'd welcome the opportunity to help raise a family, especially with Doug. This meeting could determine if their relationship would go to that next level. He was about eight years younger than her and had started having children later in life. This meant his kids were young. This excited and terrified her at the same time.

All her nerves calmed the minute the door opened and three children stood looking up at her with wide eyes and huge smiles. The blonde-haired, blue-eyed little girl reached for Jocelyn's hand, not unlike how her father did on that first date. Debbie was a darling little six-year-old girl. The two boys, Roger and Eddie, were eight and eleven.

Doug came up behind the children laughing quietly. "Shall we let Jocelyn into the house?" He took her free hand and guided her through the line of children still staring up at her. He surprised her and the children by giving her a kiss and ample hug.

"Dad." Roger giggled, turning a bit red.

Eddie said to Jocelyn, "Dad had us hide one piece of your favorite candy in each room of the house. We'll show you around, and you can look for the candy."

"And also," Debbie shouted with excitement. "We'll help you find them by telling you if you're hot or cold."

"What a fun game." Jocelyn tried to soak in this feeling for all time.

Doug headed for the kitchen to prepare dinner. Eddie led Jocelyn up the stairs, with Debbie and Roger in tow. When Jocelyn reached the sixth step, Debbie and Roger started to giggle uncontrollably. Jocelyn looked back at them. "Hey, what's so funny?"

She advanced carefully to the next step, placing her feet to either side of a piece of candy lying in the middle of the step.

Debbie let out an excited scream. "Hot! Hot! Hot!"

Roger was laughing so hard he got the hiccups.

Jocelyn pretended to look all over, except where the gold-foiled gift lay. "Give me a hint," Jocelyn pleaded.

"Look directly under your nose!" snorted Eddie.

"Oh! That *is* my favorite candy. How did you know?"

"Dad told us. He bought bunches, so I hope you get better at finding them or we'll all miss dinner." Eddie laughed.

They entered a bedroom. Roger scrambled onto the bottom bunk bed. "This is *my* room."

Eddie, in one quick movement, landed gracefully on the top bunk bed. "*Our* room."

"Could the candy be in this bed?" Jocelyn leaned over the bottom bunk and started tickling Roger. He laughed in fits and was flopping around like a fish.

"Hot, hot, hotter!" yelled Debbie as she joined in the tickling.

Still laughing, intermingled with hiccups and snorts, Roger sat up, holding his aching stomach.

Jocelyn lifted the pillow and uncovered a silver-foiled chocolate treat.

"My room, next!" Debbie yelled as she took Jocelyn's hand and pulled with all of her thirty-eight pounds.

The two boys jumped down from the beds and ran after them.

A purple hue poured out of the door, spilling into the hallway. When they entered, Jocelyn smiled. Everything was purple. The lace curtains, the rug, the bedspread, and nearly every stuffed animal piled on the bed. "I wonder what Debbie's favorite color could be?" Jocelyn smiled at Debbie.

"Purple," Debbie cried out, jumping up and down.

Jocelyn wished she could bottle Debbie's happy exuberance and drink it down. "Hmmm, where could the candy be?" She walked around the room as all three children called out directions. "Cold, warm, warmer, hot, cold, hotter, hottest!" As she approached the purple dresser with the purple elephant, Debbie yelled, "Boiling hot!"

The elephant had a candy in its upheld trunk. Jocelyn started looking under the elephant's purple belly while Roger snorted out a laugh that resulted in a huge hiccup. All of them started laughing at that, which of course, made Roger hiccup all the more.

Jocelyn thought she'd better find that candy now so Roger could catch his breath. Just then, Doug called them down for dinner. They all looked at each other for a split second and then stampeded down the stairs. When they arrived at the dining room table, all three kids fought for a seat next to Jocelyn. Doug's smiling eyes met Jocelyn's like a warm embrace.

After dinner, she agreed to read the kids a book. Debbie sat on the couch, next to her while the boys sat on the rug in front of her. As she read, she felt a little hand resting lightly on her leg. Then, she realized Debbie had snuggled up next to her and was as close as was physically possible. With no air between them, Jocelyn couldn't imagine feeling any happier than at that moment.

The entire evening had deepened Jocelyn's feelings about Doug and provided a vision of a new life of which she had never dared to dream. After that, Doug and Jocelyn saw each other nearly every day. Weeks turned into months, and they began including the children in many of their fun outings.

Doug called to say he was coming over to Jocelyn's home as he had something very important to ask her.

Was this possible? At age sixty, this happening to her? The whole thing felt like a dream someone else would have. Or a plot to a romantic comedy she'd want to watch again and again. Could this really be *her* life?

When Doug arrived, they sat on the bench outside her condo. She saw he had something in his hand but couldn't make it out. She was so full of anticipation she could hardly breathe.

"I have a big question for you," Doug began. "Well, before I ask you, I just need to clarify something that's very important to me."

Jocelyn nodded and tried to swallow, her mouth dry.

"I just want to make sure of one thing. I know you weren't raised Christian, but I need to know that you do eventually plan to accept Jesus Christ as your Lord and Savior."

Jocelyn was stunned. They knew from the very beginning they didn't share the same religion. As they'd gotten to know each other, it became apparent their spiritual values were very similar, as were the ethics by which they chose to live their lives. While not sharing a formal religion, their spiritual compatibility made life together joyful and easy.

"Doug, while I'd never actually convert, I totally support your choices for your children. I would go to the church of your choice as a family, but in my heart, I would maintain my own personal spiritual beliefs." She smiled at him and nodded for him to go on.

But he paused with the oddest expression on his face. She'd never seen that look and couldn't begin to read it. She tried to speak above the rapid beating of her heart, "What is it? Doug? What are you thinking?"

His face appeared frozen in an uncharacteristically detached expression. He looked at her, but his eyes seemed to stare past her. He didn't even look like Doug. "I'm trying, really trying hard… to fall out of love with you."

He slipped the small object from his hand into his pocket, sliding it away from sight, and with it, Jocelyn's dream of their wonderfully loving partnership. Like well-hidden candies she would never find.

A shocking jolt struck her core as she realized that, while all had been perfection to this point, this one thing was a deal breaker for him.

If this was so important, why didn't he ask her about it before the very first time he took her hand? Before he made her fall in love with him? Before he introduced her to his wonderful children? Before she ever believed this kind of happiness could actually be hers?

Jocelyn sat quietly watching his face contort while he actively fell out of love with her. Was that even possible? Could he wrench her out of his heart with a twitch of his lip?

She suddenly felt the full force of immense heartache that was now hers. She was so close to having everything she'd ever wanted. She couldn't just sit there and watch as it all slipped away. She looked at Doug and realized he was already gone to her. It was sheer agony. It was just too much for her to bear.

"I'm going inside now," she said softly, trying not to cry out of every pore of her body. "I love you and the children with my whole heart, Doug, and that will never change. What we have is a loving, spiritually fulfilling family together. I'm still very much here for you. Please think about what we're losing. But, no matter what you do, I respect your choice and only wish you and the children great love and immense happiness."

As she walked away, she knew she'd never see him or the children again. Ever. She was experiencing the death of her new family. With each step, the separation from them became more real.

For weeks, she was inconsolable. She loved and respected Doug too much to call but wanted to do so every minute of every day with every cell of her being.

In the months that followed, Jocelyn slowly began to heal. As she tried to open herself to other possibilities, she wanted to avoid another deal (and heart) breaker like the one she'd suffered with Doug. She thought about and came up with other issues that had the potential to end an otherwise seemingly perfect partnership. Of course, everyone's deal breakers were different, but Jocelyn realized it was important to learn about those areas of great personal import prior to investing a whole heart.

She knew one thing for sure. She never wanted to watch anyone else try to fall out of love with her again.

In her search for true love, like when searching for that candy, she'd gotten so very close. She could still hear little Debbie's voice excitedly screaming, "Really, really, very, very boiling hot!"

This experience gave her reason to hope it could, that it would come again.

#Click#

Chapter 20

SEARCH OPTIMIZATION

Jocelyn had a confession. She was considering crossing the street. She planned to jaywalk. Unlike that chicken who crossed the road to get to the other side, Jocelyn had no interest in reaching that destination. Her only goal: to obtain the attention of that good-looking man in that shiny new hybrid. He looked to be in his early sixties, had country music blaring, and was alone. That was it. The only information she had about him. Yet she just might walk right in front of that moving vehicle and unabashedly wave while risking life and limb, hoping he has good eyesight and quick braking reflexes.

Jocelyn knew the plan wasn't flawless, as he might not wave back. There was a nearly ninety-percent chance he was right-handed so if he did wave, there would be no opportunity to spy the all-telling wedding ring finger. She wasn't sure what she'd do if he waved, bearing a naked left hand. Jump onto the hood of the car? Or take a picture of his license and track his whereabouts later?

That's when it hit her. Not the car. The realization. She's looking. All the time. Everywhere. Even in moving vehicles. When did this searching for a mate become an obsession?

When she was married, she didn't look at all. She could remember going to a restaurant with her friend Abby. After they ordered, Abby said, "Oh my God, you didn't even notice. I'm astonished you're so oblivious."

"What are you talking about? Was there cheesecake on the menu?"

Abby rolled her eyes. "Ask our waiter for more bread and you'll understand."

Jocelyn flagged him over, requested more bread, and he complied quickly.

"Oh, you mean the excellent service? He is very attentive."

Her jaw dropped. "He's not attentive, he's gorgeous. Scandinavian model gorgeous. Good thing he's a waiter cause he's one tall drink of water that's making me very thirsty."

"Oh," Jocelyn responded with little enthusiasm. "I suppose he's good looking."

"I know you're married, but you're not blind or dead."

But everything changed after the divorce. Jocelyn was looking. Like a hungry cougar in the jungle keen to detect any movement that might lead to finding the only desirable prey: a loving mate with whom to share her life.

She abhorred this about herself. She'd always been so self-assured and self-contained. She was a successful and self-made businesswoman. After her husband left, she seemed to have lost her balance. The place that used to be her solid core was now dark and cold. While she peered out from her personal pain cave that imprisoned her when she was alone, no one else seemed to notice. Like drowning in her own black ocean with no boats in sight. No use calling out. Just tread water and search for a way back. And search she did.

For months, during each weekly brunch gathering with her single women friends, they had encouraged Jocelyn to start "getting out there."

Finally, she conceded. "Okay, you gals are right. It's time I get back in the relationship saddle. But I don't even know where to look for a steed. How do you all meet potential partners?"

Katy looked around to be sure no one else was listening. "When I food shop, I drive an extra fifteen miles to the wealthy neighborhood. I linger in the frozen food section, near the Hungry Man TV dinners."

Deb confided in nearly a whisper. "I visit my attorney's office. Often. His building has twenty-four floors, and I ride the elevator, a revolving door for rich, smart, and potentially eligible men."

One of the most shocking of all the methods Jocelyn heard came from Sarah. She was loud and proud about it. "I renovate my house. I've replaced all the windows, had new carpeting installed, and repainted four times in two years. I've changed out the tile flooring for wood and back again. I've remodeled my kitchen and both bathrooms three times."

Upon hearing this, Jocelyn was perplexed. "And this leads to meeting men how?"

Sarah smiled coyly. "You know how everyone says you have to get out there as single men aren't going to just line up at your door? Well, that's not exactly true. I call for estimates and insist they send the company's owner. Then I wait for the doorbell to ring.

"I've gone out with the CEO of a construction company, the owner of a window business, and I'm currently dating the president of a paint manufacturer. I hope he's the one as my home is exquisite, and I don't want to change another thing."

Compared to remodeling an entire home multiple times, waving at a guy in a car didn't seem that desperate. It certainly was far more cost effective.

Jocelyn came out of her reverie, looked both ways, and made herself step off the curb. She jogged right in front of the car. Luckily, he saw her in time and came to a screeching halt. She detected his left hand go up in the air while he honked the horn. She strained to see if he had a ring. It was difficult to discern as the finger prominently displayed was his middle finger. His face was red with anger.

It clearly wasn't one of the reactions she had considered. There'd be no happy ending, or even a first date, resulting from her brave attempt at flirting. Instead, she was treated to an unexpected dose of road rage. She could hardly get out of the road as she was bent over laughing so hard.

Jocelyn returned to the safety of the curb. Hmm. She supposed it couldn't hurt to try a fresh coat of paint in her bedroom.

#Click#

Chapter 21

A Picture's Worth a Thousand Dreams

Seated at an ocean-front table on the patio of her favorite San Diego restaurant, Jocelyn beheld a splendid view of sunlit beach. The breezes were filled with fresh ocean air that carried children's playful screams. The whole scene was topped by a cloudless cobalt sky with the ocean's surface shimmering jubilantly. "California Dreamin'" played gleefully in her head as she waited for Dahlia to arrive.

Dahlia and Jocelyn celebrated and endured many of life's phases in concert. Marriage, divorce, dating, starting up a new relationship, the demise of said relationship, and so on. Throughout it all, they always had two things on which they could count: optimism and each other.

Dahlia arrived. It was never hard to spot her as she had a head of wind-tossed, wild blonde hair. No matter if there was wind or not. Something about how she moved and delighted in everything gave her an air of energy and exhilaration that was contagious.

"Let me show you the new guy I'm interested in!" She called up the dating site app on her iPhone while plopping into her seat.

"Hello to you too!" Jocelyn laughed, already elated to share time with Dahlia.

Dahlia held her phone two inches from Jocelyn's face and was about to point to her new potential Mr. Right.

Jocelyn held up her index finger quickly. "Wait. Let me guess which one." Jocelyn studied the three rows of pictures displaying the twelve matches of the day. She confidently pointed to the man positioned in third place in the second row. He was tall, handsome, and wearing a suit and tie. "Him."

"How did you know?" Dahlia was astonished.

"He's *your* type."

"Isn't he everyone's type?" Dahlia laughed.

Jocelyn smiled. "Do you think he's *my* type? Okay, let's see how well you know me. Try to pick the one I'd like from your matches."

Dahlia looked them over until she came to the first one in the last row. "Him. The short one with a beard wearing a tweed jacket with elbow patches. Definitely him."

Jocelyn blushed as she looked at the picture peering back at her at the end of Dahlia's index finger. "Yes, the hippie professor; he's definitely my type."

Dahlia pushed the phone back at Jocelyn. "Write to him NOW."

"This is *your* account. He'll think it's from you."

"Okay, never mind." She took the phone back but instead of putting it away, she started typing:

Hello LastChanceForLove (his profile name). My best friend is interested in learning more about you. Her login name is Ready4uNow. If you want to meet a magnificent and mind-blowing woman, check out her profile.

When she arrived home, Jocelyn anxiously looked up his profile to read what he'd written about himself. She again looked at that one and only photo he'd posted. She became nearly obsessed with his picture, more like a sixteen-year-old rather than a sixty-one-year-old woman. His green eyes were wide and bright, perhaps signifying he was a good listener, the beard somehow worldly looking. The baldness signifying he was wise beyond his years. His chin resting on his fist disclosing the depth of his thoughts.

It was just another profile picture on CatchYourMatch.com. Somehow, she felt she knew him. He could be the one. If there was this much chemistry with a picture, just imagine the fireworks that could occur when they'd finally meet. Imagine, she did.

While she was an extremely independent, self-sufficient woman running the business she had founded, she was also extremely lonely. Not even Dahlia knew the extent of her feelings. Nor her worries for the future.

So, when she saw the face of this man in the picture and read his intelligent words, she held hope against hope that he could be as remarkable as he looked. That he, too, would be attracted to what she had to offer. It was certainly time.

When Jocelyn checked her email on the site, there was a message from him. He'd read her profile and had seen her pictures. He was interested. After a several emails and phone calls where they discovered they had multiple common interests, they decided to meet.

She'd Googled him and that same picture appeared everywhere he was mentioned. No other photo. Curious. Ordinarily a colossal red flag. But she was keeping hope alive. She just didn't know if she could withstand another let down.

Jocelyn was the first to arrive at the agreed-upon restaurant. Several people walked past her table. That one was too tall, this one had a full head of hair, the next one no beard. She normally had a bit of trouble recognizing first dates from the memory of their profile picture. This picture was crystallized in her mind. Those eyes, that beard, that face; she waited with anticipation.

"Jocelyn?" the next person to come by said, holding his hand out for her to take. This was a corpulent man, large of all proportions, except height. She searched his features trying to find the man in the picture to which she was so drawn. She tried to imagine removing several chins and a few layers of stomach. His eyes were not bright, the beard scraggly. The only thing that resembled the photo she'd memorized was this man was definitely bald.

Jocelyn took his hand. "It's so nice to finally meet you." She smiled, not at him, but at the thought, he got her with the last photo.

She'd been dating now for a long time. A very long time. She'd had enough disappointment for several lifetimes. She wanted to say, *WTF. Why don't you update your photo? Don't you mind living a lie? Do you honestly not know what you look like? Or is this a joke? Okay, I get it. You just wanted to see my reaction. You're a psychologist performing a sociological experiment to see if blind dates are indeed blind. So now you know.*

The truth was she would have actually been interested in him, exactly how he looked. If only he hadn't started out with such an overt lie. It was like she was set up to expect Robert Redford but John Candy showed up. No matter how funny and charming John Candy was, he was definitely no Robert Redford!

Jocelyn wondered if he would say something about the photo. Apologize or make an excuse for not having time to replace it. Something.

She waited.

He finally spoke, "So, what's good here?"

Once she let the shock of it all wear off, they settled into a nice conversation.

Jocelyn realized she'd have to give up the possibility of ever meeting that man she had completely fabricated from that photo. This was so infuriating. She told John Candy that while she'd had a lovely time, she wasn't willing to see him again.

"Some pictures might be worth a thousand words," she later told Dahlia, "but this picture lead to a lesson hard learned."

Dahlia laughed. "Yup, you can be creative about dating, but it's ill advised to create your date before you actually meet him."

Jocelyn suddenly remembered something. She gave Dahlia a playful, yet stinging punch on her upper arm.

Dahlia winced. "Seriously? What's that for?"

"*You're* the one who picked him out for me!" They both broke out into laughter as tears began to flow down their cheeks. Jocelyn's smile hid the real pain behind hers.

Dahlia threw her arms around her friend, giving Jocelyn an extra squeeze as they leaned into each other. It was almost as if she really did understand.

#Click#

Chapter 22

WHO NEEDS A MAN?

Since the divorce, Jocelyn had tried it all. She'd dated every available man in Florida (where she had a second home), Oregon (where she'd visited), and Southern California, or so it felt. She'd tried online dating, only to suffer the depths of digital disappointment. She'd attended multiple meetups where she'd been successful at meeting a plethora of astounding, attractive, and single …women.

Jocelyn had speed dated only to hit speed bumps. She'd gotten dressed up only to be let down. She'd gone on many first dates, never wanting a second. Then, she'd caught sight of a great looking guy in a red convertible. When she considered rear-ending him for an introduction, she realized she'd gone beyond desperate to desperado.

Jocelyn was finally ready to declare defeat. She decided to simply create a life she loved with or without a partner. Why couldn't she be happy without a man?

After all, garbage cans had wheels, furniture kits had pre-drilled holes, there were gadgets to open stubborn jars, step ladders to reach high places, and dollies for lifting heavy loads. She drove her car, even at night. She was computer literate and tech savvy with skills in videography, editing, and photography. She was very independent and had even been practicing sleeping in the middle of the bed.

Why did a strong women even need to have a man in her life? Of course, there were times it would have been far more convenient if she'd had a life partner. Like the time she caught the flu and had to drag herself to the doctor then, completely exhausted with a fever of 102 degrees, to the pharmacy. There was a long line and a long wait. She went to the woman at the counter and asked if her medications could be expedited since she could barely stand.

"You'll have to wait like all the others," the woman barked.

"Oh, okay," Jocelyn said through a cough that threatened to bring up a lung, "It's just that I'd hate to give you or any of these people this horrible flu. The doctor said I'm highly contagious." She coughed again without covering her mouth to bring the point home.

"Let me see what I can do." The woman sprinted away as if the germs were giving chase. The pharmacist filled her prescription immediately.

Another example was when Jocelyn ordered pizza the day she moved into her new apartment. There were boxes stacked high everywhere, but she decided to take a dinner break. This was her first meal in her new home. When the pizza arrived, she actually felt excited. It was the first time in her life she had ordered a whole pizza just for herself. Jocelyn savored the first few delicious bites. It occurred to her she'd never eaten pizza without anyone else present.

The expression "Dance like no one is watching." came to mind. This was a huge perk to being single. You could do everything as if no one is watching. Dance naked in the living room, leave dishes in the sink, binge watch your favorite shows, and eat what and how you please. "Yes!" she declared out loud. "I'll eat this pizza like no one's watching." She took a huge, sloppy caveman bite for fun. She giggled as she realized she had pizza sauce all over her face.

Her smile was soon replaced with a look of urgency. She'd literally bitten off more than she could chew… or swallow. The large doughy ball was lodged in the back of her throat. She couldn't breathe. She thought of calling 911, but she couldn't speak and was running out of time. Jocelyn began to sweat with panic.

Then, she got an idea. She ran as fast as she could from the kitchen to the living room. She took aim at a four-foot pile of boxes lined up against the wall and rammed into it hard with her body. A golf ball of pizza came flying out of her mouth and stuck to the mirror in front of her. "This has to be the epitome of independence," she said aloud to her image in the mirror. "I just did the Heimlich maneuver on myself."

Yes, there were times when it would be lovely (and safer) to have a partner there. But even at these times, she'd survived just fine on her own. There were a number of other perks to living the single life. A single woman living alone had the invitation to be completely and unapologetically herself. She could dress as she wanted while she went where she pleased. Life choices and expenditures were hers to determine without scrutiny.

Cooking and cleaning were optional. Problems requiring more physical strength or home maintenance skills than she had were resolved by throwing a little money at a pro. Besides all that, girlfriends were great company and a wonderful source of support, without any power struggle or sexual demands.

"Yes," she declared out loud to herself, "I don't *need* a man."

But then she sank into the newly delivered plastic-covered couch looking at the empty expanse of love seat to her left. She didn't need ice cream either, but she'd love a gallon about now.

#Click#

Chapter 23

VIRTUAL VIRTUOSO

Waiting for the next text from Steven, Jocelyn felt like a sixteen-year-old even though they were both sixty-one. Ever since they connected through Harmonius. com, there had been a daily text or emailed heart offering, a video gift of specially composed piano songs, and long, late-evening phone calls.

He was a talented pianist and teacher, respected by many of the affluent, home-schooling parents in the small, yet well-to-do coastal town in California. While not wealthy himself, he made a nice living, living nicely.

Jocelyn loved music. She also loved the fact he'd spent years becoming so accomplished. Drive was something she understood and admired in others while always demanding it of herself.

He played musical pieces combining challenging classical compositions with old standards. His fingers skillfully danced on the piano keys, with no sign of written scores. Each note seduced her senses and heightened her hopefulness.

Jocelyn was on a business trip, and he kept her company in the evenings. They had actually never met in person. Their growing relationship was completely virtual. Their "dates" consisted of digital video visits.

They laughed, made all kinds of plans including whale watching trips, weekend excursions, and the possibility of sharing long-term love.

Jocelyn's sister and confidante warned that it might just be the music Jocelyn loved, rather than the man. Jocelyn thought the music was a big part of who he was. The passion, the fullness, and the confidence that permeated from him. He could be nothing less than amazing.

He had offered to fly cross country for a first date, but now it was only a few short weeks until they would be geographically in the same time zone, in the same room, within reach. Jocelyn imagined wrapping her arms around him for the first time, adding senses like smell and touch to their growing connection.

Midmorning during a busy workday, she received a text that seemed to be written in code, by someone other than her virtual virtuoso. The text said:

Hi Jocelyn. I thought to share with you some words that have helped me: It's a new phenomenon that couples who meet online and get comfortable texting or connecting by phone find that when they meet in person, it doesn't translate. Thank you for being the generous, thoughtful, and successful beautiful person that you are. I know that you will find the right person.

She read the last sentence again as her heart began to race. *I know that you will find the right person.* At first, she thought the only explanation for this message is that he'd been kidnapped and his phone confiscated by terrorists.

She wrote back.

Are you saying you feel that you are not the right one for me? She wanted more clues as to who had absconded with his phone.

His response was in Morse code, so she invited him to talk later that evening, hopefully in the language they both had shared in the previous four weeks. She went about her day, trying not to think about this strange turn of events.

As she prepared for the video call, she tried to brace herself for the fall. Could she have so misjudged him? Was he actually trying to end it all in a cliché phrase embedded within a camouflaged text? Was it even possible that the very same fingers that danced so elegantly on ivory keys to make a piano fill a room with a melodious, full sound so beautifully could write such a staccato, off-key, tasteless, classless text message produced in pig latin?

She vowed to herself to just listen, with the only goal to understand what could have possibly happened to the man she had begun to adore.

Perhaps he had hit his head and was suffering from temporary amnesia, or it wasn't completely impossible he had a slow brain bleed that until now had gone undetected. It could be an aneurism ready to burst. This phone call could actually save his life.

She did feel an obligation to herself to consider a more realistic scenario; had she (as her sister had warned) let the music she loved affect her judgment of the man? Jocelyn thought her days of creating the man of her dreams from small remnants of the men that stood before her were long over.

Determined to actually see who Steve really was, she would listen and watch carefully, give him time to express his true feelings. Separate him from the music and see what was left. She took a deep breath, and as she exhaled, tried to release all preconceived cognitions and emotional attachment to what was about to unfold. The video call rang.

He began slowly, haltingly, and inarticulately. Something about being homophobic but also somewhat attracted to men at the same time. He told a story about his mother dressing him in a pink sweater because she didn't respect gender roles. He had played piano on cruise lines in which it would have been easier to just be with a male lover and continue that way. He wouldn't have to do what a man is expected to do when with a woman.

The ramblings moved to his religious bent. How he had to be with women of the same religion. But all those women were not interested in him because of his financial standings.

"There is just one thing I want to ask," she interrupted in a quiet voice. "Was it your intention to end our relationship with that text?"

He paused. He didn't move for a long time. She waited it out. Had the picture frozen? No, his eyes moved up to the right (she knew that meant he was trying to remember something). He stayed like that several more minutes.

She stayed equally still, trying not to smile. *Hmm, perhaps it's a stroke.*

Finally, his eyes returned forward. "Well, if I were to be honest…(pause) and of course, (pause) I want to be, but… (a really interminably long pause) …

She couldn't take it anymore. She heard her mouth release the words in quick succession. "Did you mean to break off this relationship with your text? Yes or No?"

With the momentum she'd begun, his mouth responded quickly. "Yes. I did. I didn't want to have to deal with all these overwhelming feelings. I ended it in a text!"

The image of a courtroom appeared in Jocelyn's mind. She was Perry Mason and Steve was a murderer who was dramatically driven to confess to the dastardly crime. She couldn't hold back her smile but hoped to contain it quickly.

"Steve, thank you for telling me. I now realize you have a lot of different feelings tied up inside of you. I'm not really sure how any of the things you talked about relate to me, but I am certain of one thing. The fact you were willing to say such an important thing hidden in a text lets me know I would have no interest in continuing to see you. You have a lot of work to do on yourself."

"Please," Steve said. "Tell me more. I am very interested in what you are saying."

"I am not willing to do a session with you. Please promise me you will never use texts as a way to avoid important communication. Do not do that to anyone else. It is very hurtful."

"Thank you for spending this time with me. It was nice meeting you."

Jocelyn didn't bother to remind him they actually had never really met. She decided she would never let things get this far again online without physically meeting and organically growing the connection. She also vowed to pay closer attention to the actual person and not create them bigger and better from the remnants to which she was privy.

After the call, Jocelyn realized she was crying. She was mourning the newfound hope that had died during the call. She cuddled with her dog, the only male who seemed to know how to be present, honest, and loving nearly all the time. "I'm okay," she said out loud. "It's all a learning experience. But, if I learn much more about men, I might just get a brain bleed myself!" With that she chuckled, and her dog's tail wagged. All was well.

#Click#

Chapter 24

GREAT EXPECTATIONS...REVISITED

Even as time passed, nearly three years, Jocelyn never forgot Han from the video dating service. She had tried to find him, but he seemed not to have the usual internet presence on Facebook, LinkedIn, and the like. She privately prayed he had successfully moved forward with his life and had, at long last, released the pain of losing his wife.

One hot summer day, Jocelyn was cleaning out her files when a single page of paper made its clever escape from a manila folder, extricating itself from the thickness of many other pages. It demanded her attention as it rode the fan's breeze to flutter in fits to the floor. Somewhat annoyed, yet curious, she bent down to pick up the rogue paper. The first three words leapt off the page at her, "My darling Jocelyn."

She took the letter and sat down near the lamp. The letter held the precious contents of a full and heavy heart. It poured and implored, persuaded and dissuaded her decision to leave him.

It read like a Rumi poem, seducing the reader with a longing too intimate for words, too sacred to be shared on a page.

"We are destined to be with one another. My heart does not want to beat without you by my side. I know you say I need time to get over my wife's passing, but what I need most, my sweet, darling Jocelyn, is to be with you."

She was moved. She couldn't recall even reading this when she left him three years ago. Then, on the back of the page was his signature, followed by an email address and two phone numbers. Was it possible any of those contacts were still viable years later? Should she try to contact him? What would she say?

Jocelyn typed out a light-hearted email asking Han if he'd like to reconnect. Within minutes of sending, she received a response. When she clicked on it, she saw it was a notification informing the email address was no longer functional.

Hesitantly, she called the first of the two numbers, waiting nervously; she decided not to rehearse any particular greeting. Just flow with the conversation and see what was in store for them. It rang. And rang. She was anticipating an answer, trying to remember his voice. His smile. A loud beep, then a recorded message: "This number is no longer in service."

As she dialed the second phone number, she determined that if the number worked, it was a sign they were destined to meet again. If not, she would go on with her life and put closure on the whole idea.

The familiar ring… and ring… and ring. A generic voicemail announced, "The person at this number is not available, please leave a message."

Jocelyn sat straight up and envisioned Han listening to this.

"Hello, Han. This is Jocelyn. I don't know if you remember me, but I thought it might be nice to reconnect and catch up. If you'd like, you can reach me at this number. Oh, if this isn't Han's number, kindly disregard this call." She laughed at herself and hung up the phone.

Done. "We shall see what grows from that seed." She said aloud. Was there a deity listening? Then, she noticed her dog had sat up and was watching her. "Close enough."

A few hours later, she noticed she had missed a few calls. One was showing the number she'd called earlier. She sat down to play the message and braced herself for whatever would come.

"Jocelyn." The warmth in his voice washed over her with a familiarity that betrayed the years that had lapsed. "Your message said you would like to reconnect, yet for me, we've never been disconnected. There was not a day I forgot about you, Jocelyn. For me, it's always been you."

Of all the possible responses she anticipated, this was not among them. She took a moment to quiet herself. *Be open to him.* When she had absorbed the shock of what was happening, she picked up the phone to call him.

She heard him pick up, but instead of the usual, "Hello" she just heard his jubilant laughter reaching her like a tickle from a close friend. "Jocelyn, how good to be talking to you."

"Yes, Han, I can hardly believe it myself. How are you? Are you still living in San Diego? Are you married?"

Oh my God, did I just blurt that out? Not what I had intended to lead with. She wished she could rewind back six seconds, before she opened her mouth.

"Yes and no," he responded.

"Is that like being almost pregnant?"

He laughed again. "Remember how you had told me I wasn't ready to move on with a new relationship after my wife passed? Well, you were one hundred percent correct. You told me to get counseling and join a grief group. Did I listen to you? No. I did the opposite and married the next woman I met from Great Expectations. It was a total mistake. I want you to know I had begun, months before your call, the process of leaving her and getting a divorce. Your call is a sign that I am doing the right thing by leaving this marriage."

Jocelyn was unsure of what to say. All sorts of thoughts swirled around in her head making her feel a bit dizzy.

Han interrupted her reverie. "Can I see you? I would love to see you again. There's so much I want to tell you."

"It would be lovely to see you," Jocelyn heard herself respond. Yet, she felt the need to clarify. "I understand you're getting a divorce, but you're still married, and I can't date a married man."

Han paused for a moment. "Just two old friends, then. Just lunch? A short visit that just might lead to a life of happiness for us both." He laughed again. His warmth broke the seriousness with which Jocelyn was considering this situation.

"Okay. Just lunch between two old friends." She let it stop at that.

When they saw each other, it was as if no time had passed. They hugged. The feel of him and even his scent permeated her senses and transported her back in time. They held each other for several long minutes, neither wanting to break the embrace. She forced herself to pull back, so they were face-to-face. Everything about him smiled at her. She realized her face was reflecting the same.

"Let's get a table," she suggested, feeling her face flush from the physical and emotional proximity of this man from her past.

After they had ordered lunch he began, "There is so much to share with you. Remember when we went to that boat show to look for a sailing yacht? At that time, I knew nothing about sailing, but you didn't mock me and only supported my dream. I'm so excited to tell you that I finally bought my sailboat. It's forty-eight feet and seaworthy. My goal is to sail from the California coast to Hawaii. I'm closer and closer to being able to actually do it."

Jocelyn couldn't help but get excited for him. His passion was contagious. This was a side of him she hadn't known. She loved a man who knew what he wanted and had the courage to go for it. She was more attracted to him than ever.

"Would you like to see her? She is called the *Blue Turtle*. *Blue* named after the ocean and *turtle* for me because I am slow, but steady. I have a slip at a nearby dock. Please let me introduce you to her."

"Yes, of course I want to see her." Jocelyn tried to temper her enthusiasm, but it was impossible.

When they got to the docks, Han had the key to places she had only imagined accessing. A large ornate double gate had always stopped her from visiting this secret maze of docks where magnificent yachts housed those living their dreams. The sailboats had masts that reached high into the sky while their bows were tucked comfortably into their own personal slip. Han's boat had a custom-made cover that protected the whole deck from saltwater, rain, and gifts dropped from above from a variety of birds. An indication that he took very good care of her, this precious manifestation of his desires.

Every wooden board on deck and below had been refinished painstakingly yet lovingly by his own hand. He'd replaced the faucets and appliances, put in a system for hot and cold water, and a shower for daily comfort. The boat was immaculate in every nook and cranny. It looked brand new. There were two bedrooms, a galley, and a full bathroom below. It was bright with white leather sofas and windows that let light and air flow in.

"Han, I'm so happy and proud for you. This is what you've wanted for years, and you made it happen. You are now truly the captain of this beautiful boat and your life. There's nothing you can't do." Jocelyn burst with happiness for him.

"Thank you, Jocelyn. It means so much to me to have you on this boat. It's only you that's been missing. With you present in my life, my total vision of what life could be is now possible."

They sat together, and he put his arm around her. She placed her head on his shoulder and felt an excitement in every cell of her body that she'd not experienced in years. It was like arriving home after such a long, lonely journey. They sat like that in silence, each imagining the possibility of them living this life together.

He turned to her to kiss her tenderly. Her body responded without her permission. They shared a moment of passion as if they were two teenagers with no control of this force between them. As if suddenly waking from an amazing dream, they both came to their adult senses, the reality of the situation rudely interrupting this blissful reunion.

"We'd better go," Jocelyn whispered, trying to recover and regain control.

"Yes, we should go." Han said softly, all the while smiling happily. "We will have plenty of opportunity to be here together soon."

After what happened, or nearly happened on the boat, Jocelyn decided until the divorce was final, she would only see Han during daylight hours for a walk or for short visits in very public places.

They saw each other once a week, but each time they got together, his wife would call and interrupt their time together. It seemed he was unable to ignore the phone or was just unwilling to pay the high price for doing so. It became painfully clear that he was not emotionally free, and his wife did not understand or agree with his plan to divorce. The delays in filing the divorce went on and on.

In the meantime, Han wanted assurance from Jocelyn that they'd be together as soon as the ink dried.

"Have you taken the time you need to be on your own?" she asked him.

"Well, not exactly. I met Gretchen two days after you and I said goodbye. We were married a month later." His gaze went downward.

"Han, after my divorce I spent a whole year on my own. I learned so much about myself and gained more confidence for being alone. This helped me make better decisions. I know this is what I told you three years ago, but I still think this would be of great benefit to you. You could take the boat and live your dream."

"*You* are my dream."

"My dream requires two equally strong, independent people who love and support each other. You could be part of that dream, but it's important to take the time to gain confidence and become that independent person. Do you understand?"

"We would be strong together. I would never leave you. We could do anything if we are together."

"Did you feel that way about Gretchen when you married her?"

"Yes."

"What happened?"

"She was the wrong person."

"I'm so sorry, but you moved very quickly with her because it was scary for you to be alone. And now you're choosing me, perhaps for the same reason. Until you take the time to be on your own, you are the wrong person for me."

When Jocelyn left, she felt bad. For both of them. But something inside her knew this was his second chance to become his own person. She realized there was a time she would have jumped at the chance to marry someone who said, "I will never leave you." She had grown. She had become bigger than her fears. She wanted this for him too.

#Click#

Chapter 25

INVITATION TO DINNER...OR BOOTY CALL?

Jocelyn arrived at Starbucks in a run. She was five minutes late, and she didn't want to waste any of her precious gal-pal time with Dahlia. She found Dahlia already seated with Jocelyn's favorite chai tea waiting for her. Dahlia didn't want to waste any of their time together either.

As Jocelyn sat, she asked, "How was your date with Ocean Front Guy last night?" They had names for all the men they dated such as Body Odor Dude (AKA BO Dude), Flyboy (a retired pilot), Doc (not a doctor, but liked to "role play"), Fit N Funny (he was neither), Shady Guy (Obsessed with fifty shades of something else), Smelly Feet (no explanation needed), etc.

Dahlia took a deep breath. "So, I want to tell you something, but you have to promise not to get mad."

"I rarely get angry with you. Not since the time you got in that guy's car on the first date and went to his house. You called me from a locked bathroom and asked me to come rescue you. You'd never do anything that stupid again, so I'm cool. You can tell me anything. You know that. What happened?"

"Well, of course I didn't get in his car. I sort of drove myself to his house. I know I shouldn't have gone on the first date, but I wanted to see his ocean-front mansion. Curiosity got the best of me. I mean you would expect a man who can afford such a home to be a classy gentleman. Right?"

Jocelyn was shaking her head in disbelief. Rule number two. Stay in well-lit public places for at least the first three dates. But her disbelief turned to concern. "Are you okay? What happened?"

"Everything was going fine. You wouldn't believe that neighborhood. Most gorgeous homes I've ever seen. All with ocean views. Amazing. The front door alone probably cost more than my whole house."

"Give me a tour later. What happened?"

"Sorry. Well, we were cooking dinner in the most incredible kitchen I've ever seen—"

Jocelyn interrupted. "I get it. The house was nice. What transpired, and do we need to call the police?"

Dahlia laughed nervously. "Nothing like that. I was lucky. I was at the stove. I'll tell you about the *stove* later." She smiled coyly. "I was stirring the sauce, looking out the window at the ocean view thinking *I could get used to this* when, all of a sudden, this guy had eight arms, and they were all over me. Two seemed to hold me in place, two found their way to the girls, and the last two were travelling South of the Border. That's when I realized I was in trouble. Not only with you, but real trouble."

"And?"

"I turned towards him. I told him in my sexiest and quivering voice, 'Hey, mister, my sauce is boiling over, and I need to focus. Could we have that for dessert?' He smiled, winked and released me."

"That was so smart."

"I learned from the master. I told him I had to use the restroom to wash up. He took over at the stove, and I snuck out the front door and ran to my car. Thank goodness for my escape vehicle."

Jocelyn breathed a deep sigh of relief. "I'm glad it ended well. It could have been bad. I'm so glad you kept your head and lead him to believe there was no reason to force himself on you."

"I've learned my lesson. Stay in public view until he earns my trust. I was just so curious what his house looked like. It was magnificent. Too bad he comes with it."

"To celebrate your survival, how about I show you a safer way to view those incredible homes. We can go to a few open houses this weekend. We won't need to stir the sauce or deal with an octopus to take a fun tour."

"Great idea. I'll bring a picnic, and we can sit on the beach afterward."

Jocelyn pretended she was over it, but she couldn't help running all the possible scenarios over in her head. She loved Dahlia and couldn't stand to think of her in harm's way.

Dahlia was glued to her phone.

"Are you finding open houses for this weekend?"

"Not exactly. I just found a new dating site called, MillionaireMatches.com. Look at this guy."

As Dahlia showed her the screen, Jocelyn realized they would need to have another talk about how people easily lie and post works of fiction to attract unsuspecting singles. Dahlia was smart and funny. She also was way too trusting. She'd already had two close calls. Jocelyn hoped to keep her safe while navigating online dating.

#Click#

Chapter 26

Doctor, Lawyer, Indian Chief

Jocelyn decided, after all this time, it was her turn to meet her "happy ending" guy. After all, she had met bad-dude guy, liar-liar pants-on-fire guy, married guy, retread guy, rebound guy, BO guy, and even a guy who wasn't a guy.

It was time for her to have the big online-dating success story you always hear about. You know, the one everyone describes when telling the story of how a divorced daughter met a great man online. "He's a dentist with a home on the beach in California and a ranch in Colorado."

The guy your neighbor met. "He's a wonderful person who just happens to be a doctor who just sold his thriving practice for millions."

That one who took one look at your friend's niece and asked her to marry him on the spot.

Even the eighty-five-year-old grandmother who met a man when she fell and couldn't get up in the food store.

They've been going on back-to-back cruises around the world ever since.

She just had to believe after several years of doing this that it was her turn. She perused the online profiles. There was one man who stood out. He was sixty-nine, a newly retired eye surgeon with a second professional degree in law. He was obviously intelligent, nice-looking, divorced, and living at the beach near her. Seth was also Jewish. Jewish, a doctor, and a lawyer. This was the Jewish mother's trifecta.

She wrote him, and he replied immediately. After a few days of emails, they graduated to phone calls. The first time they talked, the conversation lasted two hours. It seemed there was no end to their commonalities.

On their next phone call, Seth shared one thing that was normally a very red flag. He disclosed that his age was actually seventy-four, not sixty-nine. He explained that no one would respond to him if he told them he was in his seventies.

"But you are in your seventies." Jocelyn reminded him. Another inconvenient truth. It did bother her that he had lied on his profile. Normally this would be cause for dismissal. It's just that everything else about him made him her very own potential happy ending guy.

They made plans to meet. He was busy that weekend, so they agreed to go out on Monday evening. They went out to dinner at a small restaurant/bar. It was definitely not fancy, but the food was delectable. She enjoyed the banter, laughter, and shared wit. He was the first man she'd met that challenged her intellectually.

When Seth asked Jocelyn out again, she said she was free on the weekend. Seth said, "Oh, I have previous commitments this weekend, but I can get together with you during the week."

Jocelyn found a Florida Groupon for an airboat through the Everglades, something they both had wanted to do. Several alligators later, they made their way back to Jocelyn's house. They spent hours sitting out on the patio looking out at the water, observing the ducks, geese, turtles, and egrets.

It was peaceful and easy being together.

They were planning their third date, and Seth again told Jocelyn he would not be available on the weekend. She asked for more details.

"My cousins live up in Boca Raton, so I spend each weekend with them."

"You stay in Boca every weekend?" Jocelyn was curious as to why he did this since his home was in Fort Lauderdale, a mere thirty-minute drive from Boca.

"They are the only family I have out here. I don't really enjoy them since we end up fighting about politics all the time," he explained.

This didn't make any sense to Jocelyn, but she didn't know how to get more information without pushing. She'd wait and find a way to bring it up again.

For their third date, Jocelyn found a meetup that offered a class in swing dancing. She loved dancing, and it would show her how open he was to trying new things. The meetup was on a Monday night, so he was available.

This, too, was fun. Afterward, she asked him if he'd like to get together over the next weekend. "I have a commitment this weekend," he replied.

"Are you married?" she heard herself blurt.

"No, of course not. I just have a… complication, if you know what I mean."

"Actually, I don't. I need you to explain what this complicated ongoing commitment is?"

"Well, it's …" He stopped.

She waited. Ready for the other shoe to drop.

He continued, "A relationship that I'll be getting out of soon." His eyes were glued to the ground.

Jocelyn felt her heart drop but demanded her face not reveal her upset.

She asked him, "Does *she* know this?"

"It's been mentioned." Still not making eye contact. "We've gone back and forth many times. It's not working. I just never expected to meet a 'you.' I will end it, but there are commitments I've made that I have to keep."

Oh my God. Her doctor-lawyer-happy ending was turning into a lying, cheating wimp right before her eyes. This was a metamorphosis she could have done without. She just couldn't abide finding her happy ending this way. This would lower the bar so much that if she attached a cloth, she could mop the floor with it.

She couldn't hold back; she told him outright, "I don't do this to other women. Men seem to be thinking of one thing when they lie and cheat. Themselves. I have to think of that other thing. The woman to whom you are doing this. I simply don't do this to other women."

When she got home, she asked her Amazon Echo, "Alexa, play the song, 'I hate men.'" Alexa complied. Jocelyn only suspected from personal experience there would have to be a song by that title. Of course, she was right. It was a Broadway song that was hysterical. Only this wasn't Broadway, and it wasn't at all funny. And this definitely wasn't Jocelyn's happy ending.

Doctor-Lawyer guy had become Doctor-Lawyer-Liar guy. She wasn't looking for a doctor or a lawyer. She'd even be wary of an Indian Chief, if he were a man.

#Click#

Chapter 27

Praying for Patience

While walking her dog, Jocelyn noticed her new neighbor, Maria, exiting her front door. At first Jocelyn considered just continuing on by, as the dog pulled against the leash with some urgency. She was new to the neighborhood and felt an obligation to get connected to her new community. She guided the dog across the street to greet this tiny Hispanic woman with a vibrant smile and undeniable aliveness.

"I couldn't help but notice you live alone," Maria began slowly and carefully, locking eyes with Jocelyn as if she were going to disclose something very important. "If you want someone to be with, it's very simple." She paused, trying to read Jocelyn's receptivity to her wisdom. She leaned in and nearly whispered, "You just need to ask God for what you want. He's always there and will provide exactly what you ask."

Jocelyn reached out and touched Maria's arm. "If you don't mind me asking, what is it you asked for?"

Maria smiled involuntarily. "I was praying to find a husband. I asked for just three things in a man. First, that he knows God. Next, that he would love and be kind to my children. Lastly, that he be a hard-working man. I didn't care about money, just those three things."

"And is that what you got?"

Maria laughed. "Yes. Jose is a wonderful husband." She paused and looked to see if anyone could hear her before she added, "But, if I had it to do over again, I would have also asked that he have a little money." Then added, in case God was listening, "He's hard-working, so it is okay." Her eyes went toward the sky. "Perhaps if he had money though, he wouldn't have to work so hard." Laughing, they hugged and parted ways.

As Jocelyn finished her walk, she thought about if Maria's benevolent God happened to ask her, "What three specific qualities would you like me to send you in a mate?" What would she answer?

She had tried to whittle down her list, her top expectations of a potential mate, to a reasonable top ten. The perfect man for her would be honest, loving, kind, intelligent, emotionally and financially stable, calm, communicative, healthy, and happy.

Maybe this was her problem. She was still looking for the perfect match. Was there even such a thing? Certainly, she hadn't found evidence of it when she asked her women friends about their husbands. When she asked if they were happy with their partners, she usually got one of two responses. Either they'd burst into tears and unload a series of shocking truths about what occurred behind closed doors, or they'd say they were happy and loved their partner deeply.

Jocelyn would then say, "I'm so happy for you. I'm curious, though. If you could change one thing about him, what would it be?" She was amazed how quickly the answers came. Most often, it was not limited to one thing either. Many included benign yet perpetual complaints like "I wish he'd pick up his socks. They're all over the house, all the time." Or, "I'm actually thinking of supergluing the toilet seat down." To more serious infringements like "I just never know when he's going to blow. We don't go out anymore since I can't risk him raging at me in front of friends."

The mantra of the married? "No one is perfect."

Was finding a mate like trying to find a pair of shoes that would have to be worn til death do us part? Does one have to sacrifice style for comfort? Take the low heel to retain balance or choose the great-looking stiletto and become a fall risk?

Mooji, a spiritual master, was once asked by a disciple, "How can a single person find her true-life partner?" The audience went silent with anticipation.

Mooji sat thinking for a moment, his hand thoughtfully on his chin. Finally, he spoke. "My advice is this; enjoy being single while you can. Sometimes finding a life partner can become a life sentence." He exploded into a great belly laugh as did the audience. After taking a deep breath he quieted and said, "Stop looking. Enjoy your life. When it is right for you, the correct person will find you."

Jocelyn did love her life and enjoyed the freedom of being single more than ever. She also knew herself. She wanted more than anything to share her adventures with one person she knew, trusted, and could call family.

She began to realize she repeatedly "fired" potential partners rather quickly. This one was too nervous on their first date, that one had really bad breath, this other one seemed obsessed with his weight, while this other one was too boastful and pushy. That one had a lizard tongue…the worst. Perhaps she should have given them the chance to show her who they really were over time.

Jocelyn decided that she'd make a new practice of patience and tolerance. She'd overlook things that ultimately held little import. Things such as crooked teeth, balding heads, idiosyncratic behaviors, and nail biting. She'd choose sneakers over heels to go the distance in the long run.

She got back on the horse, her computer. She made an online connection with a man who appeared from his dating profile to have many of the qualities she sought. He was a retired doctor with grown children and young grandchildren. He owned a nice home within a few miles of hers, was within a compatible age-limit, a non-smoker, and social drinker. They talked on the phone, and he'd made intelligent and pleasant conversation. His picture literally wasn't pretty, but as long as his character was attractive, that was what mattered. Her goal was to practice increased acceptance and give him a chance.

As they were arranging to meet, Jocelyn asked him to which restaurant he'd like to go.

Ben replied, "You pick the place, and I'll pick you up."

"What type of food do you like?" she asked.

"Whatever you pick is fine."

She started to wish he'd contribute to the task of selecting a place but caught herself in mid-judgement. He was just being accommodating. She self-corrected.

"I'll be coming from a visit with my mother so let's meet there," Jocelyn told him, as she had learned to never provide her address to a person on a first date.

They met at the Greek restaurant Jocelyn had selected. She'd researched and found this restaurant was halfway between where they each lived. You walked in, you could smell the feta cheese, olive oil, and garlic hanging in the air. It was delicious.

They'd had a great conversation that lasted several hours. They were the last to leave. Ben was a gentleman and didn't even kiss her after walking her to her car. It was a pleasant evening, and Jocelyn was actually excited about the possibility. She was very comfortable with him, and the communication had flowed easily.

The next day, they made plans to meet again. She invited him to a concert. Even through the texts, she could tell he wasn't enthusiastic.

"Would you prefer to do something else?" she asked him.

"Do you want to see a movie?" he asked.

"Sure," she answered. "Always up for a good film."

"You pick it, and I'll pick you up." He responded.

"I have an idea. Why don't you pick the film?" She hoped to sound light rather than challenging. "As long as it is not too violent, with some intelligent dialogue, I'll be happy." She was trying to make it easy for him.

A few minutes later, she got a text. "What movie would you like to see?"

Seriously? Man up! Have an idea. Contribute. I mean, why did she need a man if he made her do all the heavy lifting? She looked in the mirror. *Stop it!*

She got on the computer and found one that was not violent but also wasn't a chick-flick. When he offered to pick her up, she again said she'd meet him there.

Then her phone let her know there was another text. "Would you like to meet for dinner before the movie?" he had written.

Finally! Jocelyn brightened. He was exhibiting some leadership! See, she just needed to give him a little time to show his real colors.

"Sure." Jocelyn texted back happily. "There's lots of restaurants near the theater. We can go to one of them at seven as the movie starts at eight-thirty."

He texted right back. "You pick the restaurant, and I'll meet you there at seven."

Arrrrggghh. Hopeless. She threw the phone onto her bed.

Jocelyn took a deep breath and reminded herself to have patience. She picked up the phone and typed. "I'm in the middle of something. Can you just Google restaurants near the theater and pick one? I'll meet you there."

About ten minutes later a text came in forwarding a listing of three Chinese restaurants. "These are the first three that came up. Which do you like?"

When she looked at them, they were all at least ten miles away from the theater.

She couldn't take any more texting or indecision. "I'll just meet you at the theater at eight for the movie. If we're hungry we can get something afterward."

They arrived at the theater within minutes of each other. While getting some drinks at the snack bar, Jocelyn found herself gagging from the very strong scent of cigarettes nearby. She turned to see who was reeking so she could move away from the noxious odor. But as she turned to look, the only one there was Ben.

"Do you smoke?" she heard herself say a bit too loudly.

"I just smoke a little." he replied.

She couldn't stop her mouth. "Either you are or you're not. Either you smoke or you don't."

"Since I'm in the process of quitting, I checked non-smoker on my profile. I mean what if I do quit and my profile says I'm a smoker? Many women don't like smokers, so what am I supposed to do?"

"You're supposed to write the truth. You smoke. If you quit, then, you can change it to reflect the truth." She was unable to even look at him. He had lied in his profile and now wasn't even owning up to the fact that he smoked.

She remembered her goal of tolerance. Could she possibly be with a smoker? Worse, could she be with someone who lied about smoking? No. This was too much.

They watched the movie in silence. She was glad she had her own car waiting for her. Although, admittedly, she was disappointed her tolerance policy hadn't even lasted long enough to get to their seats.

This was a long-term partnership she was seeking, not a melon from the food store. While one could tolerate a bruised melon skin and the tang of over ripeness, should a person sacrifice her core values just to avoid a little loneliness? Yes, no one is perfect, but she had to be true to herself.

As she watched him walk away, she envisioned Pig Pen from the Snoopy gang with a cloud of smoke hanging like an aura as he walked to his car. She was still alone but happy as she took in a slow, deep breath of fresh air.

#Click#

Chapter 28

WHO WEARS THE PANTS?

There were so many pitfalls to dating, Jocelyn wondered why she was still at it. She had a beautiful life. A nice home, friends, family, and a career that kept her challenged and creative. It was just that she was tired of having to do everything herself, from taking out the garbage to always driving when she went out. She felt alone and out of place in a world populated by couples and families.

It's not that she couldn't handle her own life. But there were times when she just wanted to put on her soft, silky slacks rather than always wearing the "man pants." She knew how to make repairs around the house, handle the minutiae that came with home ownership, and caring for an aging parent.

She just wanted a sweet partner in her life to share the joys (and chores). Someone who would be willing to sometimes wear the pants in the family. Take some of the load off her shoulders.

It was the first time she spoke with Jonathan. The voice at the other end of the line was so warm and laughed so easily, Jocelyn just knew his eyes were smiling. When she checked the clock, it had been over an hour, yet it felt like mere minutes since the phone rang.

They exchanged witty banter like an exciting tennis match. Instead of balls sent back and forth, it was a game of words with a brand-new partner. He served an excellent opening remark about the weather. She returned his serve with a high lob about hobbies; he runs back and hits a beauty as they discover they share several interests. She decided to play the net. This was a dangerous move, but she moved close and dared a question about politics. He gave her the point as they discovered they both leaned toward the same party. Score: One Love.

By the second hour, they were finishing each other's sentences. The conversation flowed easily, leaving barely enough room for a silent moment. Even in those rare quiet gaps, she heard him breathing. Surprised how even his inhalations were synced with hers.

It was the first time they spoke, but it felt more like a reunion. He said out loud what she was thinking. "I love your confidence, how you think, the sound of your voice. We need to meet. What are you doing tonight?"

She laughed at Jonathan's childlike enthusiasm. This was far more refreshing to Jocelyn than a game where players held feelings like a closely kept secret. Yet being guarded when meeting a new man has been trained into her. They agreed to meet the following evening.

She learned the hard way not to spend too much time relating in a virtual mode. If you email, text, or even talk on the phone over a long time, it makes it more difficult to transition to a face-to-face connection in 3D reality.

Like that guy, Augustus, who called her every evening while she was on a two-week business trip. They both enjoyed the phone visits, and she couldn't wait to meet him in person. But when she returned home, each time they made plans to meet he called at the last minute to cancel. Finally she asked, "What's really happening here? Don't you want to get together?"

He hesitated and then admitted, "I'm afraid to meet you. This is already the best relationship I've ever had. I don't want to ruin it by meeting."

She told him she didn't want a phone buddy and ended it right there. She expected if he was real, he'd call back and show up. She never heard from him again. He got to keep his memory of their wonderful phone relationship, and she got to learn an important lesson. While you need to learn enough about a man before meeting him in person, don't wait so long that you establish phone rapport that doesn't translate to real life.

Jocelyn now made it a practice to email a few times, graduate to a phone call or two (asking the most pertinent questions), then set up a physical meeting at a very public location.

So when it came time for her and Jonathan to meet in person, she was trying to come up with suggestions for what they should do on a first date. Her friend Gail called to invite her on a sunset sail. Gail was thrilled to add Jocelyn's date to the group. All of Jocelyn's married friends lived vicariously through her stories about online dating. This was an opportunity for them to see the ritual up close and personal.

She called to invite Jonathan to the party, and plans were all set for a potentially romantic evening.

The boat was beautiful and large enough to accommodate all eleven guests. They set off just as the sun was low in the sky, with everyone helping to raise the sails. After a few hours of visiting with the other guests, a light dinner, and a gorgeous orange sunset mirrored on the water's surface, Jonathan and Jocelyn went to the bow to sit together and talk.

They enjoyed the conversation as they had done on the phone. When there was a lull in the conversation, she decided to ask Jonathan a question to stimulate additional sharing.

"Jonathan," she began. "What is one thing you want me to know about you?"

She used to ask men, "What is one thing you *don't* want me to know?" But that question lead to things better not revealed so soon, or at all. The result was never good, so she posed this in a more positive way.

"Well," he said without much hesitation. "I caught my wife in bed with my best friend."

"Oh." She said sympathetically. "Was that what lead to your divorce?"

"Not right away." His head went downward as his eyes stared at the water lapping on the side of the boat.

"You tried to make it work after that?" She asked.

"No. We were over. But I stayed with her for thirty more years."

She was trying to make sense of this. "You had children together? You stayed for the children?"

"No. I'm not sure why I stayed. She made me move into the basement while she continued to see my best friend. I stayed friends with him, or it would have been very awkward."

"That must have been miserable for you."

He seemed to want to say something, but hesitated.

"What is it?" She encouraged him to open up.

"I kind of liked it. I always had a fantasy of being 'the weak link,' if you know what I mean?" He looked at her for some sign of understanding.

"Not really." She admitted. "What does 'weak link' mean?"

"I like a strong woman." He hinted.

"I'm sorry. I'm going to need you to tell me more. I'm a strong woman, but I don't think of the man as a 'weak link.'"

She thought she noticed his face turning a bit red.

"Okay." He was definitely blushing. "I like to be mistreated. I like to be submissive. To be dominated. While it was a painful experience, it was kind of a turn on for me."

She tried really hard for her face not to divulge the deluge of thoughts screaming in her head. *Oh my God! Seriously? Is it so hard to meet one normal guy? At least this is a new one. Nope, haven't encountered S&M before. Just the ordinary ones like lying about his age, cheating on his wife, registered as a sexual predator, doesn't like dogs. OMG, I really hope no one on the boat heard any of this.*

She realized he was waiting for some kind of reaction. All she could manage was, "Looks like we're almost back to the dock. Let's go back and see if they need any help."

They both got up and headed to the stern of the boat. Everyone was looking at her with anticipation since they knew it was a first date, and they were curious about how it was going.

She acted as if all was good.

All of a sudden, she started laughing at the irony of initiating this date looking for someone to "wear the pants in the family" and ended up meeting a man who clearly wanted her to wear the man's pants.

#Click#

Chapter 29

Breaking up Is Hard to Do...
Unless You Have a Smart Phone

Jocelyn had been trying to come up with a way to break up with a man once she realized they didn't have chemistry. She laughed at a *Seinfeld* episode when George started saying, "It's me; it's not you." She laughed harder when the "George," AKA Sam, she was dating at the time actually said it to her. "It's me; it's not you."

She answered without hesitation, "You're right. It is you."

Mostly she was very ineffective at initiating a breakup. She wanted to let Sam down very gently. He was still very hurt and sad from his last breakup. He talked about it all the time. He broke into tears often, and she tried her best to console him, but she was less and less enamored.

She met him face-to-face. "Sam, you are a really great guy. You're sweet and kind. You're also very attractive. I just think we're not a good fit. I'm sure you will find happiness soon."

He called her the next day and said, "You made me so happy with all the wonderful things you said. I'm so glad I found you. Would you like to take this to the next level and go away with me for the weekend?"

He had only heard the positive things she said to soften the blow. He missed the blow entirely. Now she was going to have to break up with him all over again!

She found out that men and women had entirely different approaches to the breakup talk. Actually, the way men did it involved very little talk. In fact, it seems customary these days for men to inform a woman of the relationship demise in a text. A convenient, to the point, thumb-typed message, press the send button. All the messiness for them disappears.

Jocelyn couldn't believe this until it happened to her. She had been seeing Pete for nearly a month. He was very quiet. His shyness made it difficult to get to know him, so she was taking it slow. Apparently, too slow for him. Although they did kiss, he hadn't made a physical move towards her either. They were supposed to go out that night, but instead he texted, "This is going nowhere. Best to cut it off now." Period.

She wrote back, "If by 'it' you mean our relationship, I agree. I'd never want to be with a man who would breakup in a text."

He never replied. Over and out. Way simpler than her method that required multiple conversations and lengthy consoling sessions.

There are certain codes, Jocelyn learned, related to the breakup. If at the end of the conversation the breaker says to the breakee, "I hope we can remain friends," this actually means "You'll never hear from me again."

Other breakup codes were:

"Let's do this again sometime." (You will never see me naked.)

"I think we should take this slower." (He's seeing someone else.)

"Perhaps we should start seeing other people." (He's already seeing other people.)

"Maybe we should take a break." (A pre-emptive breakup.)

"I've really enjoyed getting to know you." (A covert breakup.)

"I'm going to be out of town for a while." (Liar, liar, pants on fire breakup.)

He just stops calling, texting, or emailing. (The chicken-shit breakup.)

Typically, most breakups end with "Good luck." (Meaning? You're gonna need it.)

Jocelyn thought of a better way. What was the truth of most breakups? Next time, if there was a next time, she thought to say, "You don't meet my needs, so I am breaking up with you. May we both find what we seek." She realized that last part was just another way to say, "Good luck to us both!"

Nah, she'd gift the next one with a consolation prize of a marble rye and say clearly, "We are over. It's not you, it's not me, it's George!"

#Click#

Chapter 30

Two-Thousand-Mile Date

When Jocelyn checked her morning emails, she found one from MeetYourMatch.com. It said, "Truly enjoyed reading your profile. I sense we may be searching for the same ending. Thoughts? Wayne."

This was an improvement on the typical one-click response like a smile or a heart or a waste of keystrokes that just said, "Hi." Or the very telling first message of, "Oh baby, what you do to me." Or "I'm wrecked by that body of yours."

While she ignored most of those messages, she immediately opened Wayne's profile to learn more. After all, he had written full sentences. In English. With punctuation marks. She saw he was nice looking, articulate, and seemed to be sincerely seeking a relationship.

She wrote him. He responded immediately. In each communication, they learned they had an unusual amount in common. They discovered they actually lived within two miles of each other. They shared the same religion. They both had selected careers that used American Sign Language. This was rare and exciting. They decided to meet.

While they both lived in Florida, Wayne was currently visiting his children in Minnesota. He would return the following week. By then, however, Jocelyn would be flying to California to take care of some business and visit friends. They agreed to keep in touch with phone and FaceTime calls and meet upon their return.

On the next phone call, she had news. "I'm going to have to stay in California another three weeks. I guess if you want to have a first date sooner than that, you'll have to fly out to San Diego," she joked.

The next morning, he texted, "I made a reservation."

She was shocked. And not too sure how to respond. It might be fun to show him around her favorite city. But what would his expectations be?

She called him. "Are you serious?"

"As a heart attack."

She laughed. "Let's hope it's more fun than that! So, we need to clarify some things up front. You're flying two thousand miles for a first date. It is a first date. You should know I don't sleep with guys on the first date. While you'll be here for three days, the whole thing is a first date."

"Duly noted. Thank you for taking the pressure off both of us."

You'll need to get a hotel room since I'm camping out in my house, sleeping on the only bed in the place."

"No problem. It's best if we have our own space for when we are not together."

"San Diego's public transit system is not the best. It could take two hours to go four miles. If you don't mind, it would give you a lot more freedom if you rent a car. This is going to be one expensive date. It's okay if you don't want to do this."

"I'm almost packed. No turning back now. Although, if I were completely honest, I'm a bit nervous about what might happen if we don't get along."

She was concerned about the same thing. He could fly all that way only to discover, usually within minutes, they wanted nothing to do with each other.

She said, "Okay, let's agree that one of two things will happen. Either we become really good friends, or something way better occurs."

"That sounds great. Especially the 'way better' option."

They both laughed, and the tension fell away.

"Wayne, let me know your itinerary, and I'll pick you up at the airport."

He paused. "Thank you, but I'm getting in late. I'll Uber to the hotel, and we can meet in the morning when I'm fresh."

"Don't be too fresh!" They laughed easily now.

While Jocelyn was experienced with online dating, this was a first. No one ever boarded a plane to go on a first date with her. It was romantic, exciting, titillating...and terrifying. Would this be her next big blunder, or would this be the story, they would tell for all the happy years they'd be together. Only time would tell.

In the days preceding his arrival, she imagined various and sundry possible scenarios. Her favorite was walking toward the hotel just as he came out the front door. The moment their gaze met for the first time, an orchestra erupted with Whitney Houston singing "Greatest Love of All." Their faces simultaneously exploded into exuberant smiles. Walking toward each other, their pace hastened. They found themselves in a slow-motion run culminating in an embrace that lasted for all time.

Of course, there were other versions of this meeting far less appealing and a plethora of possibilities: a disastrous date with someone she'd spoken to once on the phone. This was either the most romantic thing she'd ever done, and the gods would reward her for having such faith, or this would go down in the dating history books as the blunder of the century. Only time would tell.

The day finally arrived, as did Wayne. She drove to the hotel to meet him. She got out of the car, turned toward the hotel to see him come out of the door. She paused, waiting for Whitney to start singing. Nothing.

As they walked toward each other, they did each smile. She feigned running in slow motion. He laughed. They hugged hello, but instead of eternity, it lasted the customary three seconds.

Okay then. Plan B.

Jocelyn had arranged for them to go on a two-hour cruise around San Diego Bay. She figured this would be a good start to a potentially twenty-eight-hour date. If it wasn't good, only twenty-six more hours to go.

The cruise was lovely. Wayne had insisted they pose for the picture as they boarded. They reached for each other's hand as they strolled around the ship. The sky was a palette wash of blue with only an occasional wisp of white as sea gulls flew overhead seeming to peek from above to see how things were going.

The cool ocean breezes, blue sparkling waters, and clear sunny sky made the journey festive and happy. It was perfect.

"Thank you for arranging this wonderful and unique view of San Diego." Wayne wrapped his arms around her and gave her a long hug. She leaned into him and put her head on his shoulder. It was comfortable and comforting.

When they disembarked from the ship, he insisted on purchasing the photos taken earlier. He gave her a set and kept one for himself.

It was late in the afternoon when they returned to the car.

"What's next, captain?" He asked.

"Well, I was thinking we'd head over to Seaport Village. Jet lag may be setting in about now since your biological clock is still on eastern standard time. So, your choice: sightseeing or a nap?"

He smiled at her as if he'd just swallowed a Cheshire cat. "Yes. Nap, please. I'm wiped. Thank you for being so sensitive."

She was no stranger to that cross-country commute, nor the effects of jet lag. She'd also enjoy a short break on this marathon of a first date.

As he got out at the hotel, she told him, "If you're up for dinner, I made reservations at one of my favorite hangouts on the water. We can watch the sun set over the ocean, unlike the sunsets at Fort Lauderdale beach.

Jocelyn was feeling hopeful as she recounted the day. He seemed nice, sweet even. So far, no red flags or idiosyncratic behavior. This experiment with spontaneity was going as well as could be expected (although Whitney Houston had still not made an appearance).

Wayne had rented a car and insisted on driving them to dinner. That was fine by Jocelyn.

When they arrived at the restaurant, Wayne excused himself to go to the restroom. She waited for his return. They were seated at the table she had requested by the window with a beautiful view of the harbor. There was a special on lobster which they both ordered. Before the food arrived, he excused himself to go wash his hands. She began to get concerned but didn't say anything when he returned.

They were having a nice conversation, enjoying the food and each other. About halfway through the meal he said, "Excuse me" and got up from the table.

When he returned, she asked him, "Are you alright? Do you need to leave?"

He smiled shyly as he reddened a bit. "No, thank you. I just have a little OCD and when I become anxious, it helps me to wash my hands. I also take about three or four showers a day."

"Nothing wrong with cleanliness," she said, trying to put him at ease. She knew that obsessive compulsive disorder was no laughing matter. There could be a lot more to discover regarding the impact this had on his life.

"While we are on the subject, you should know I like chewing gum."

She didn't understand why this might be a problem.

"I chew gum all the time. From the moment I awake to bedtime. Only when I eat do I stop. Also…"

Please stop! She was screaming inside her head. She put all the meat from the lobster tail in her mouth to keep the scream from escaping.

He kept talking, "I don't really eat."

She looked on his plate. That lobster looked back untouched, mirroring her puzzled expression.

"I was grossly overweight, so I had lap band surgery. Give me your hand."

She hoped he was going to give her his lobster. Instead, he placed her hand on his stomach. She felt something hard protruding out through his shirt. Her impulse was to pull her hand away, grab his lobster and make a run for it.

"That's a port they can use to adjust the lap band and if needed. My stomach is very small so I can barely eat. Once I'm at my goal weight, I'll have them loosen it a bit."

"That's interesting," was all she could manage. The day had gone so well, they should have quit while they were ahead. She checked her watch. Only twenty-four more hours to go.

She secretly hoped he would start laughing and tell her everything he just said was a bad joke. Instead, he excused himself and headed for the bathroom. While he was gone, she took and ate his lobster.

Normally, this would have been the end of the first date and Jocelyn would have gone on with her life. But this man had flown 2,600 miles and spent nearly a thousand dollars for this perpetual date. She felt obliged to see it through. Besides, it wasn't his fault he had OCD. Perhaps she could learn to accept the inconvenience of it and have compassion for the suffering it brought him. She'd sleep on it and try to make the best of the next day together.

In the morning, she showed him around La Jolla. The Cove was bustling with tourists. This was the kind of day people flew thousands of miles to experience. The water was clear turquoise and so inviting that Jocelyn asked Wayne, "Do you like to swim?" If his answer was yes, they were going in, bathing suits or not.

He replied, "Well, back in 1968, or was it '69, no it was actually 1967, I was in high school, no, it was junior high, and I joined the swim team. I wasn't very good. But my grandfather, on my mother's side, no I mean my father's side, was captain of his swim team. He won many awards for his swimming ability. I always felt badly that I didn't make him proud of me because I wasn't a very good swimmer."

"What I meant was, the water looks delicious and is unusually warm for San Diego. Would you like to go in the water?"

"No."

It was interesting that usually when she came down to the Cove, she looked longingly at the couples there, sad that she was alone at such a beautiful place. Right now she was part of a couple, but she would love to be alone so she could go in that beautiful water.

They headed back to the car. He talked as they walked up the hill. "It's interesting but in 1958, no maybe it was 1962, I went to San Diego. We went to the zoo. Or no, I think it was Sea World. Oh, I just remembered, it must've been in the seventies. Anyway, when I came, I met this friend of my mother's neighbor, or maybe it was a friend of my neighbor's mother. Anyway, we visited La Jolla Cove on that trip."

Jocelyn said nothing. She couldn't. She was biting her tongue so hard she was afraid if she opened her mouth, blood would come spilling out.

"Then," he continued mercilessly, "at about 1975, or was it 1976, my uncle Joe had decided that he was going to retire and move his family down to Florida. Well, my mother really loved that idea, so she started making plans for us to move down as well. But, my cousin, Franny, had a boyfriend. Joe or John, no it was Jake. Franny was sixteen, or maybe she was seventeen, and didn't want to leave Pennsylvania."

He took a breath but before he could continue, Jocelyn interrupted him.

"Wayne. We are in the most beautiful place in Southern California. I'm afraid you are missing it by always going back in the past. We are here now. Look around. It's so picturesque with sea breezes in your hair and sun on your skin. Hear the seagulls and see the pelicans diving for fish. The seals are playing in the surf, riding in the waves. And I fear you are missing the whole experience because you are back in 1967 or 1968."

She checked his expression to see if she had said all of that out loud. Yes. She had. He had a look of being taken aback, but just for a moment.

He said, "I like going back. In fact, this reminds me of 1998 when there was a huge storm, and right after that it was so calm you could hear a pin drop. Everyone came outside and just looked at the sky. It was a day very much like today. Or maybe it was in 1999.

Okay, OCD or incessant gum chewing was not a reason to break up with someone. But being excruciatingly boring was. Mission two-thousand-mile, three-day date: abort, abort!

"That's interesting," she heard her polite self return to the scene. Eight more hours to go.

When he left the next day he said, "When you get back to Florida, we'll reconnect and see what happens."

"Sounds good." She was just glad her three-day dating sentence was complete, and she was now emancipated. She learned to limit a first date to a local geographic and a more finite amount of time. As much as she usually begrudged her single status, she was happy to return to it as this date had felt like a long, bad marriage.

#Click#

Chapter 31

CAN I GET A RIDE?

Coming home from a long plane trip, Jocelyn landed in San Diego. She thought of Adam along with all the nice things he'd done. They'd become friends over the years, even though he'd married several years ago. She knew if she asked, he would happy to come pick her up. She was in the mood for some good karma. Jocelyn called him.

His wife, Robin, answered. Jocelyn should have put together a reminder script. She hadn't planned on what to say in case his wife answered.

"I'll get Adam for you," she said to Jocelyn, knowing who she was.

Along came Adam. His voice was so loud and happy.

"If this is a bad time, I could call a cab and probably get home safely or make it part way there before getting raped," Jocelyn told him.

"No. I'll leave in a few moments. It'll take it only ten minutes."

In a few minutes, Jocelyn got into a very comfortable car with a smiling Adam at the steering wheel. Finally, away from all the strangers and the family. It was an enjoyable, all-too-short of a trip. They laughed and bantered the whole way home.

Until Adam told Jocelyn that his wife had greeted him with the news that she had been having an affair for two years and wanted a divorce. She was already in love with Larry, one of her grad school instructors, and she didn't care too much about Adam. Jocelyn heard the whole story on that ride home.

She thought the best way they could support each other was by having dinner together. They could commiserate on the ways it felt to be greeted with an empty house or by one that was filled with a companion who wanted out.

They made a date for Saturday, which Jocelyn quickly forgot about.

Saturday came, and she was sitting in her sweats watching TV when the doorbell rang. Confused, she answered the door and was surprised to see a smiling Adam, nicely dressed and carrying a Trader Joe's key lime pie.

He must have noticed her puzzled expression. "We had a date, remember?"

Her face heated with embarrassment. "Come on in. I've apparently forgotten. I'm so sorry. I haven't prepared anything."

Adam laughed as he stepped inside. "Why don't we go get Mexican food in Old Town San Diego?"

She agreed and ran to change. Dinner was great fun. They cried and laughed about things that happened to each of them. Then they talked about the kind of things they wanted to happen in their lives. A lot of trips, a lot of dreams.

After dinner, they planned to meet again. For Jocelyn, it was so they could continue to get to know each other as friends. But she suspected that for Adam, it was really about getting to know Jocelyn as possibly more than a friend.

They went back to her house for that key lime pie. Adam ate half the pie. He came at her to kiss her, with lips open.

She pushed him away. "I am sorry, it's been a really long time, and I don't just kiss anyone. Thank you for taking it slow."

He smiled and fell asleep on the couch.

Jocelyn wasn't sure what to do, so she wrapped him up in a blanket. When they woke up the next morning, Adam cooked them a great breakfast.

They had both also gotten an email from Robin. In fact, the whole New Special Church did. It said, "Last night Jocelyn stole my husband, Adam, by sleeping with him."

Jocelyn decided not to respond, not to expand the drama.

The reverend called a little later. He said someone had once done that to him. He chose the same response and felt the silence had made his comment the best way ever—without words.

Jocelyn told him they both appreciated his call of support. She told him not to share this, but the two of them slept separately. She didn't feel the need to share this with the whole church.

It was the best course of action they could have done. No words, no struggle. Robin looked for a reaction, and they didn't feel the need to offer one. They were not in the wrong. They were free.

That evening, they went on their next date. They went dancing. Jocelyn had a girlfriend who had a dance floor. The room had wooden dance floor, a sound system, and even a disco ball. A waltz was playing. Adam and Jocelyn stepped onto the floor and began dancing.

They waltzed around to the right, to the left, peering into each other's eyes. The song was long; it was a great dream. All the past was gone, all the people in the room had disappeared. It was only the two of them. Only the song and their movement together. None of the questions, none of the answers. Only the presence of Adam and Joycelyn. When the music stopped, that did not interrupt their dance. When they finally realized it had stopped, they only saw who was in front of them. Each other.

The dancing stopped, and the kissing began. That was all there was. There was nothing to hold them back from each other. They kissed and hugged, oblivious to anything or anyone around them. These kisses were the first but not the last.

Jocelyn continued to see Adam. She realized she was a woman strong enough to know what she needed and strong enough to go get it.

#No More Clicking#

Chapter 32

WHAT'S IT ALL ABOUT, JOCELYN?

Journal entry:

I'm amazed how unhappy and lonely I feel while spending time with the men I've been meeting. This journey began immediately following my divorce. I only wanted to go back to "normal" by finding a life partner. I believed settling down would resolve the overwhelming angst I was experiencing. I finally realized that finding a man, if not the right man, was not the answer. It may fill my house but not fulfill my soul.

When I was married, I thought I was happy. The truth is, while I liked having him there when I came home, my life was really about my work. Many women my age had families and their work took the form of raising children and managing a household. I now also see that, for me, my company was really the place I escaped to. What was I escaping from? The business was all encompassing, constantly challenging, and left little time to focus on myself. Building a company helped me avoid building a life.

While I thought these victories at work defined me, it was a complete distraction from my real inner work. It's one thing to strive to accomplish things and quite another to try to become one's whole self. The things we acquire become old, take up space, and prevent us from moving on. All the pressures and successes become a list of things we've done. In the end, even the details of our worthy accomplishment begin to fade, as do we.

Perhaps a loftier goal would be to attain answers to questions like, who are you when you're not busy doing? How do you feel when all the noise stops? If you take away the business of life, the work stops, the kids grow up and move on, or the husband is gone. What's left? Who is looking back at you in the mirror?

Of course, even when you're totally alone, there are ways to avoid yourself. When I was first by myself, the silence was deafening. I had to have the constant chatter of television, watching other people live fun and exciting lives. I didn't know how to be in silence. I didn't know how to just be inside my own life. It was terrifying.

While searching for the right man, I finally began to answer those questions. In each Mr. Wrong I found out so much more about who I am and what I want, need, and choose for my life.

Our life is like a blank book we are each gifted at birth. Our only real job in life is to write our story. To fill those pages with thoughts, feelings, love, adventure, silence, connection, work, community, giving, receiving, nurturing… creating a soulful character that we can love and celebrate.

It's not about finding Mr. Right, it's about being the most right you. They say you get what you give. If I am so desirous of love, I need to find avenues for giving that to others. Perhaps finding the kind of authentic, deep, and abiding love I have to give doesn't begin with a first date at all. It might not even involve a man.

It might be dedication to a job, a woman, a final cause, a home to learn how to be, art, anything you love to do.

To a strong woman, it could be anything at all. Your book is waiting to be printed.

#Not a Click#

EPILOGUE

Fifteen minutes late for a service, I tiptoed into the back of the sanctuary of the church I had called home and excused my way through an aisle to a vacant seat. Looking toward the front where our choir was performing, I noticed someone new off to the side. There stood a petite woman sporting a mullet. Interesting choice of hairdos, I mused.

She was gesticulating poetically with her hands and making what seemed to me at the time funny faces in time to the choir's music. It didn't take long before it dawned on me this tiny woman was using American Sign Language in service to our small-but-active deaf congregants. She was petite, but her use of sweeping arm motions and her little bounce in time to the music made her loom large in the room.

She went on to interpret the rest of the service with the same passion (sans the bouncing, of course). At the end of the service, the minister thanked the choir and the interpreter Jenna aka Jocelyn (The character Jocelyn in this book is based on Jenna's dating experiences.) After the service she went one way, and I went another way, and that was that for a while.

Months later, Jenna and I found ourselves together in a class. She sat across from me as a part of a large circle of fellow students. Even from across the room I sensed a sadness in her eyes. It was disconcerting to see. When asked to break into pairs to practice one-on-one listening, somehow Jenna became my partner. We paired off and got to learn about each other.

I learned she had moved to San Diego to get away from the cold, wet weather of the Oregon winters. I learned she had founded a successful ASL media company. She had two dogs and a cat and loved them more than anything else. She then shared her husband of many years had left with very short notice, leaving her shocked, confused, and alone. She was heartbroken.

I comforted her as well as I could. When class was over, Jenna went in her direction and I in mine. This was true in more ways than in which directions we walked away.

Jenna was quiet, mature, and focused. I, to the contrary, had none of those traits at the time. I was living and loving the life of being a local rock star, singing and playing keyboards in a moderately successful—but wildly fun—blues band. My lifestyle came with all its trappings of sex, drugs, and rock and roll. I was definitely not a catch in the eyes of someone as stable as Jenna appeared.

All of that began to change when out of the blue I got a surprising call. It was Jenna. She was at the airport, and she asked if I could give her a ride home. Of course I agreed, and thirty minutes later we were driving to her house, talking away about who knows what when it hit me. I sort of liked this tiny, blue-eyed, beautifully smiling woman.

When we arrived at her house, I walked her to the door, and we hugged. I asked to see her again, and she invited me to come to dinner later that week. I danced back to the car and drove home with my head and body abuzz with possibilities.

The day of the dinner was upon me, so I bought a bottle of wine and a key lime pie from Trader Joe's and drove over. I rang her doorbell and waited. When she opened the door, I noticed a look of confusion on Jenna's face. She had totally forgotten about her invite, so there was no dinner.

I was awkwardly invited in nonetheless. I presented the wine and the pie. We sat and talked, and when we got hungry, we ordered a pizza delivered. When it was time to leave, I leaned in for a kiss and was rewarded with a small peck on the cheek. Still, I was excited to have met someone so different from the women I had dated. Jenna was different. I could talk with her.

We next found ourselves in a class where we voluntarily sat next to each other, and for the next six weeks we flirted and giggled and undoubtedly disrupted the class. I think everybody noticed, but we couldn't help ourselves. The rampages of a young love blinded us to proper church-like social behavior, but we just couldn't help ourselves.

We started dating seriously after that. Then came disagreements, which had us both in a lurch. This went on for decades. This book is the chronicle of Jenna's escapades in dating during the many times we were apart. Still, both of us could not let go of each other. We kept coming back together and separating again over and over. We were stuck to each other; like it or not, we were in each other's lives forever.

In time, we became inseparable. I loved Jenna aka Jocelyn to no end almost immediately. We were a passionate couple. What I mean by that is we talked, we loved, we cooked, we giggled and fought through issues.

Without our arguments and our falling outs, this book would not have existed. Over a course of twenty-three years, Jenna and I always loved each other. We could never get away. And we tried!

Finally, I realized that Jenna was an alpha female and resistance was futile. So I stepped back and became a source of comfort and tried to be a safe place for her to land. It wasn't easy sometimes, but as I would tell her, "It was always you, Jenna. No matter how long we are together, it wouldn't be long enough."

Sadly, on January 28, 2020 after a small episode of Jenna having trouble speaking, we found out she had an aggressive brain tumor. Cancer. Incurable. Over the course of the next twenty-two months, we tried everything we could think of. But eventually it got the best of her, and she died in December 2021.

This book is a look through a small window into Jenna's brilliance, writing abilities, and insight into the human condition while searching for true love. Which I have to add, was right in front of her from the day we met. I am proud to have been her "Adam," her husband and best friend… Well, her best friend most of the time anyway.

She will forever be in my heart. That beautiful woman was my once-in-a-lifetime love. Read this book and see a bit of what I saw in this amazing woman.

Loui Michael Cassell-Pane

Made in the USA
Las Vegas, NV
29 November 2022